The
Cichlids
Yearbook

Volume 3

Ad Konings (Editor)

CICHLID PRESS

1		
2	3	4

Cover photographs:
1 - *Herichthys tamasopoensis* Artigas-Azas,1993 in the Río Puente de Dios, México. Photo Juan Miguel Artigas.
2 - *Crenicichla jegui*, Rio Tocantins, Brazil. Photo Frank Warzel.
3 - *Pseudotropheus* sp. "Zebra Goldbreast", Charo, Lake Malawi, Malawi.
4 - *Neolamprologus leleupi*, M'toto, Lake Tanganyika, Zaïre.

Mary Bailey (Crediton, UK)
corrected the manuscripts and
translated the German articles

The editor wants to thank the following persons who supplied various cichlids for photographic purposes:
Peter Baasch (Stegen, Germany)
Marc Danhieux (Mal-Ta-Vi, Hohenahr-Erda, Germany)
Alain Gillot (Zaïre Cichlids, Kalemie, Zaïre)
Stuart Grant (Lake Malawi Cichlid Centre, Salima, Malawi)
Edwin Reitz (Aquapport, Ronnenberg, Germany)

Distributors:

USA: Old World Exotic Fish, Inc., P.O. Box 970583, Miami, Florida 33197
UK: Animal House (U.K.), Ltd., QBM Business Park, Birstall, Batley, West Yorkshire WF17 9QD
Australia: Riverside Aquarium, 16 Ninth Avenue, Campsie 2194, N. S. W.
Sweden: Fohrman Aquaristik AB, Odds Väg 7, 433 75 Partille
Germany: Aquapport (Edwin Reitz), Köselstraße 20, 3003 Ronnenberg
France: Africa, 9 Place Duberry, 92390 Villeneuve La Garenne
Netherlands: NVC, Lieshoutseweg 31, 5708 CW Stiphout

ISBN 3-928457-13-6

Cichlid Press, 6837 St. Leon-Rot, Germany

CONTENTS

Introduction

The third volume of the Cichlids Yearbook has been put together by 19 authors and nearly every one of them has visited the habitat of the cichlid(s) they write about. One of the main strengths of the Yearbooks is the fact that everything is first-hand knowledge and not information gleaned from other books.

Those authors who have contributed for the first time are briefly introduced in the same order as their articles appear:

Annette Bentler (Hohenahr-Erda, Germany) is employed by Mal-Ta-Vi, the largest cichlid wholesaler in Germany, and has spent several months in Tanzania in order to organise shipments of cichlids from Lake Nyasa (as Lake Malawi is still called in Tanzania). She reports on an attractive new mbuna.

Jörg Freyhof (Bonn, Germany) is a specialist on West African cichlids and has made several expeditions to that region. He has also visited the *terra typica* of *Hemichromis letourneauxi* in Egypt and reports on this gorgeous cichlid.

Jaap-Jan de Greef (Parish, Florida) is a hobbyist who visits Central and South America at least twice a year, purely for fish. These are collected and taken back to Florida where he breeds them and distributes them among other aquarists.

Kaj Andersen (Dronninglund, Denmark) has made several expeditions to South America and reports on the collecting of *Pterophyllum altum* and on other cichlids from Colombia.

Tonny Brandt Andersen (Brønshøj, Denmark) is chairman of the Danish Cichlid Association and occasionally visits South America. The famous photographer Ingemann Hansen accompanied him on his last trip and supplied several photos for both Danish authors.

For the first time the Yearbook contains descriptions of cichlids that are new to science. Juan Miguel Artigas (San Luis Potosí, México) describes a cichlid of the Río Pánuco drainage system whose existence he has known about for more than 15 years. I have written a revision of the Malawian genus *Sciaenochromis* in which three new species are described, among them the popular "Electric Blue".

Gerard Tijsseling has constructed an under water housing for a video camera that resists the pressure at a depth of 200 metres. He joined me on a trip to Lake Malawi where we tested the heavy housing. Gerard had built it in such a way that, after connecting it via several 200 metres-long cables, we could see on a TV-screen in the boat what the camera was filming in the depths of the lake! Although the weather didn't co-operate we were able to take some shots of *Synodontis* and an occasional cichlid at a depth of 90 metres. After its first successful descent we dubbed the housing Nkolokolo which is the local name for *Synodontis*. With another underwater housing I was able to film many cichlids during their day-to-day activities. Some of them and the deep water shots can be seen on a video that has been released recently.

The "Nkolokolo". Photo Iemkje Tijsseling.

Without the hospitality and co-operation of several friends it would have been impossible to show you the cichlids in their natural habitat and give you first-hand information on how they live. I am therefore grateful to Stuart Grant (Salima, Malawi), Alain Gillot (Abidjan, Ivory Coast), Gary Kratochvil (San Antonio, Texas), Juan Miguel Artigas (San Luis Potosí, México), and Mireille Schreyen (Bujumbura, Burundi).

Ad Konings

TANGANYIKAN CICHLIDS

The *Neolamprologus brichardi* complex

Ad Konings

Neolamprologus brichardi photographed in its natural habitat near Magara, Burundi.

When the first *Neolamprologus brichardi* were exported from Lake Tanganyika in 1971 (Brichard, 1989) they received the apt trade name of "Princess of Burundi". These elegant cichlids were collected in Burundi near a place named Magara and although they didn't possess the bright coloration of other, at that time common, aquarium fishes, their marvelous finnage made the Princess one of the most popular cichlids among aquarists. It proved to be an excellent aquarium resident even though it is a territorial species which defends its domain with quite some persistency. Given the right amount of room a pair will soon breed and produce successive broods of offspring. This is the most pleasant part of maintaining this species because older juveniles actively help their parents in defending younger fry (Staats, 1972). This also occurs in the lake where large aggregations of breeding adults inhabit a certain part of the rocky habitat. Most adults live and behave like monogamous pairs; it is the sheer number of pairs that sometimes gives the impression that *N. brichardi* is a schooling cichlid.

In 1952 the Princess of Burundi became scientifically known as a subspecies of *N. savoryi*, namely as *Lamprologus savoryi elongatus* (Trewavas & Poll, 1952). In 1974 Poll raised the Princess of Burundi from subspecies to species level. Realising that the name *L. elongatus* was already occupied —*Lamprologus elongatus* (now *Lepidiolamprologus elongatus*) had been described by Boulenger in 1898— he named the Princess of Burundi *Lamprologus brichardi* in honour of the late Pierre Brichard who had discovered numerous Tanganyika cichlids. In 1985 Colombe and Allgayer published their revision of the genus *Lamprologus* in which the Princess of Burundi was moved to *Neolamprologus* and Boulenger's *elongatus* to the revived genus *Lepidiolamprologus*. They argued that now that Boulenger's *elongatus* was no longer in the same genus as that of the Princess the old subspecific name of *elongatus* could be used again. For just one year the Princess was named *Neolamprologus elongatus* until in 1986 Poll published a revision of all Tanganyika cichlids. He accepted the new generic name *Neolamprologus* of Colombe & Allgayer but changed the scientific name of the Princess

back to *N. brichardi*. His reason was that the name *N. elongatus* was already occupied by yet another *elongatus*. In 1909 Steindachner described under the name of *Julidochromis elongatus* a cichlid which was removed by Boulenger to the genus *Lamprologus* in 1915. *L. elongatus* had already been described so Boulenger had to rename Steindachner's *elongatus*. He named it *Lamprologus steindachneri*. Poll assumed that Steindachner's *elongatus* was a member of *Neolamprologus* which meant that that name should have priority over that of the Princess of Burundi, which therefore once again became *Neolamprologus brichardi* (Poll, 1986). In 1988 I found out that in all probability Steindachner's *elongatus* —the type of *Julidochromis elongatus* had reportedly been lost— was a synonym of *Lamprologus callipterus*, for this reason I changed the name of the Princess back to *N. elongatus* (Konings, 1988). Fortunately Burgess (1988) put an end to the Princess' misery by simply noting that the name *elongatus* was not available when it was given to her for the first time in 1952. As he pointed out, this was a mistake because the name *elongatus* had already been used for Boulenger's *L. elongatus* in 1898 and also subspecific names compete with specific names for priority. So now, once and for all, the

Neolamprologus savoryi at Magara, Burundi.

Princess of Burundi is scientifically known as *Neolamprologus brichardi*.

Simultaneously with the description of *L. savoryi elongatus* another subspecies was described, namely *L. s. pulcher*. The difference between the two subspecies is based mainly on the pattern of the markings on the gill-cover. Both species have two dark bars between the eye and the outer edge of the gill-cover. In *N. brichardi* these bars have roughly the shape of the letter T lying on its side (see photograph). In *N. pulcher* the bar directly behind the eye is not horizontal but curves downward and does not merge with the vertical bar on the edge of the gill-cover. *Brichardi*-like cichlids have been exported from Zambia, the southern part of the lake. Some of these fishes were sold as *Lamprologus pulcher*. It is, however, not known whether these were caught at or near the type locality (which is unknown) or just looked like the holotype of *L. savoryi pulcher*.

Over the years Horst Walter Dieckhoff and I have gathered a good number of photographs of many different populations of *N. brichardi*-like cichlids from all around the lake. Comparison of these pictures showed me that those gill-cover markings differ slightly between all populations (see also accompanying photos). Even the population at Kasoje, Tanzania, don't show the exact markings as drawn for the holotype of *L. savoryi elongatus* which was reportedly collected at this locality. It thus seems that the markings may differ in the preserved state from those in the living fish.

One species in the *N. brichardi* complex is easily recognisable and does not show (up to now) geographical variation, i.e. *Neolamprologus savoryi*. This small species, with a maximum size of about 8 cm, is identified by the broad vertical bars on its body. It was found at every rocky locality visited. It prefers a depth between 10 and 40 metres which is somewhat deeper than that for *N. brichardi*, which is seen mostly between 5 and 25 metres. *N. brichardi*, and all the other races or species in the complex with markings on the gill-cover, occurs in large groups. *N. savoryi*, however, is usually found in pairs or solitary and is frequently seen close to groups of the other species of the complex.

In the last 20 years many different *N. brichardi*-like cichlids have been exported under various names. We have seen *Neolamprologus* "Kasagera", "Daffodil", "Walteri", "Mbitae", "Black Brichardi", "White Tail" or "Palmeri", "Cygnus", and others which have not yet been

Neolamprologus falcicula at Magara, Burundi.

Juvenile *N. falcicula* at Magara have an orange dorsal fin reminiscent to that of *Neolamprologus* sp. "Cygnus".

A juvenile of *Neolamprologus* sp. "Cygnus", a possible geographical variant of *N. falcicula*.

mentioned in the aquaristic literature. All these variants or species are reportedly collected at different locations.

The first reports that, besides *N. savoryi* and *N. brichardi*, another species may inhabit the same biotope came from Brichard (1989). After many years of collecting at Magara, Burundi, he found that another *brichardi*-like cichlid lives at levels deeper than 15 metres. This species, named *Neolamprologus falcicula* (Brichard, 1989), lives in pairs or in very small groups, usually not far away from large groups of *N. brichardi*. The most important difference between these two

Neolamprologus falcicula (*Neolamprologus* sp. "Walteri") photographed at Cape Kabogo, Tanzania. Photo H. Walter Dieckhoff.

species is the lack of gill-cover markings in *N. falcicula*. The cichlid with the trade name *Neolamprologus* sp. "Walteri", found in Kigoma Bay and at Cape Kabogo, is a geographical race of *N. falcicula*. At present *Neolamprologus* sp. "Cygnus" from Cape Mpimbwe, Tanzania (see Yearbook vol. 1), is also regarded as a geographical race of this species. The orange-yellow dorsal and anal fins of the juveniles of the Magara population of *N. falcicula* are somewhat reminiscent of the wonderful juvenile colours of the Cygnus. *N. falcicula* was never seen in large groups except in the case of the Walteri in Kigoma Bay, but here too they hover never more than 10 cm above the substrate, whereas *N. brichardi* may be seen one metre above the rocks.

In his book "Cichlids and all the other fishes of Lake Tanganyika", first published in September 1989, Brichard mentions of other localities where *N. brichardi*-like cichlids share the habitat with a similar species. These localities are on the southwestern shores of the lake. In his book Brichard describes an additional four new species, all from this area. Heinz Büscher, who has visited this part of Lake Tanganyika many times, also reports (1989) on a third or possibly fourth species sharing the habitat with *N. savoryi* and *N. brichardi* (and another *brichardi*-like

cichlid). He described this species as *N. marunguensis* which must be regarded as a synonym of *N. crassus*, described several months earlier by Brichard. Brichard uses several morphometric characters to distinguish between these species, which is of course the normal practice in such descriptions. When we look at these new species we may notice that the gill-cover markings differ from species to species (see photos). Personal observations in the natural habitat indicate that the individuals of any one population do not show any apparent variation in the pattern of these markings. Therefore we can take these markings as a diagnostic feature in the identification of any of these species.

Brichard also reports that at Zongwe, Zaïre, *N. brichardi* shares the habitat with *N. splendens*. Latter species —its trade name is "New Black Brichardi"— has distinct markings on the gill-cover (see photo) and can thus easily be recognised and distinguished from *N. brichardi*. But I could not find cichlids with *N. brichardi*-type markings on the gill-cover at Zongwe. I saw three species of the *brichardi* complex at Zongwe: *N. savoryi*, *N. splendens*, and *N. gracilis*.

N. splendens is a dusky coloured cichlid. The gill-cover markings are in the pattern of a V and are not much different to those found in *N.*

Neolamprologus splendens at Kanoni, Zaïre.

Neolamprologus splendens at Tembwe, Zaïre. Note the V-shaped markings on the gill-cover.

savoryi. Büscher showed me a photograph of a juvenile *N. splendens* which has vertical bars not unlike those of juvenile *N. savoryi. N. splendens* may therefore be more closely related to *N. savoryi* than to *N. brichardi.* Its maximum size is about 8 cm. Although it is common in the rocky habitat it was not seen in huge numbers as is sometimes the case with *N. brichardi.* The photograph on page 147 of "Tanganyika Secrets" (Konings & Dieckhoff, 1992) shows *N. brichardi,* and not *N. splendens* as indicated. *N. gracilis* lacks gill-cover markings and is further recognisable by the very long filaments on the unpaired fins. Some sub-adult individuals have caudal fins almost as long as the standard length of the fish. This is the main feature that sets the species apart from *N. crassus,* which is much stockier and lacks the filamentous fins. This species, like *N. gracilis,* lacks the markings on the gill-cover. It is a rather small species with a maximum size of about 7 cm. Its type locality is at Lunangwa, but it is also found at Kapampa and in Moliro Bay, Zaïre, and at Cape Chipimbi, Zambia.

The very interesting community at Kapampa, Zaïre, has already been discussed, with regard to *N. caudopunctatus* and *N. leloupi,* in a previous volume of the Cichlids Yearbook (1992). At Kapampa, where these two species share the habitat, *N. caudopunctatus* has a yellow dorsal fin, perhaps to distinguish itself from *N. leloupi.* A similar situation exists between *N. crassus* and *N. gracilis.* Both these species lack gill-cover markings, but *N. crassus* has broad white-blue edges to the dorsal and anal fins (Büscher, 1989; see photo). The filamentous tips of the caudal fin are white in both species although they are much longer in *N. gracilis.* The latter species is more elongate than the more stockily built *N. crassus.* At Kapampa *N. crassus* lives at a rather deep level of the rocky biotope. Büscher (1989) reports that it was found mostly between 25 and 35 metres. *N. gracilis* was also observed at the same location but in shallow water at about 10 metres.

Neolamprologus gracilis at Kanoni, Zaïre.

Neolamprologus crassus at Kiku, Zaïre.

Neolamprologus gracilis at Kapampa, Zaïre.

This geographical variant of *Neolamprologus crassus* at Kapampa has been described as *N. marunguensis*. It is found sympatrically with *N. gracilis* and *N. brichardi*.

Neolamprologus brichardi at Kapampa, Zaïre.

Neolamprologus sp. "White Tail" or "Palmeri" is found at Kibwesa, Tanzania (Dieckhoff, pers. comm.). This cichlid is without doubt a geographical race of *N. gracilis*. It is not known whether another *brichardi*-like species is found in the same habitat or not.

At all other known localities where three species of the complex share the habitat, there are *N. savoryi*, a *brichardi*-like cichlid with markings on the gill-cover, and one without any such markings. It thus seems that the possession of these markings or the lack of them is the main feature which segregate the species in the complex (apart from *N. crassus* and *N. gracilis* at Kapampa).

The types of Brichard's descriptions are deposited in the Museum voor Midden Afrika, Tervuren, and the four species from Zaïre (*N. splendens, N. gracilis, N. crassus,* and *N. olivaceous*) all have the type locality Masanza on the label ("2nd bay north of Masanza"). In his description of *N. olivaceous* (also spelled *olivaceus* in the same publication) Brichard (1989) mentions the bay of Luhanga (=Lunangwa), Zaïre, as the type locality. At Kiku, which is north of the Lunangwa River, I could find only *N. brichardi* and *N. crassus*. The photograph on page 375 of his book shows a specimen of *N. olivaceous* which agrees with the preserved types and with the *brichardi*-like cichlids I found at Cap Tembwe, Kitumba, and M'toto. It is therefore possible that either the type locality lies south of the Lunangwa River (which could not be confirmed by Büscher (pers. comm.)) or the designation of the type locality as Lunangwa (Luhanga) is an error.

The characteristic markings of *N. olivaceous* consist of two vertical curved bars on the gill-cover (like chevrons). The bar directly behind the eye borders the pre-operculum just as the second bar borders the outer edge of the gill-cover (see photo). This pattern is characteristic

Neolamprologus sp. "Daffodil", which is here regarded as a geographical variant of *Neolamprologus pulcher*, is very well established among hobbyists.

The Zaïrean population of *Neolamprologus pulcher* has been described as *N. olivaceous*. (Photo taken at Kitumba, Zaïre).

This aquarium specimen of *N. pulcher* is exported from Zambian waters.

At Cap Tembwe, Zaïre, juvenile *N. pulcher* have orange dorsal fins.

of *N. pulcher*. Although the type locality of *N. pulcher* is unknown the gill-cover markings of this cichlid are seen in several populations. I therefore propose to regard *N. olivaceous* as a synonym of *N. pulcher*.

N. pulcher is a small cichlid (maximum size about 6 cm) which lives in small groups in the somewhat deeper rocky habitat. Most individuals were seen below 10 metres. Juveniles at Cap Tembwe, Zaïre, have orange dorsal fins. *Neolamprologus* sp. "Daffodil" found at Kalambo, Tanzania/Zambia have similar gill-cover markings and yellow unpaired fins in juveniles as well as in adults. Because of the apparent

Neolamprologus brichardi at Kiku, Zaïre, have attractive orange tips on the tips of the unpaired fins.

importance of the pattern of the gill-cover markings I consider the Daffodil a geographical race of *N. pulcher*.

N. brichardi seems to have the widest distribution of all the species in the complex. I regard all *brichardi*-like cichlids with T-shaped markings on the gill-cover as geographical variants of *N. brichardi*. V-shaped markings are found in *N. splendens* and chevron-shaped markings in *N. pulcher*. *N. falcicula* is recognisable by the lack of markings on the gill-cover and by the black outer edges of the dorsal and anal fins. *N. gracilis* lacks the markings as well but has white edges to the unpaired fins. It differs from *N. crassus* in its elongated body, the depth of which is 25 to 28% of the standard length (Brichard, 1989). The comparable percentage in *N. crassus* is 30 to 35%.

It is interesting to note that thus far *N. brichardi*, *N. gracilis*, and *N. pulcher* have a discontinuous distribution and are found on the west as well as on the east coast of the lake.

References

BRICHARD, P. (1989) *Cichlids and all the other fishes of Lake Tanganyika.* TFH, Neptune, U.S.A.

BÜSCHER, H. (1989) Ein neuer Tanganjika-Cichlide aus Zaire. *Neolamprologus marunguensis* n. sp. (Cichlidae, Lamprologini). *DATZ* 42, pp: 739-743.

BURGESS, W.E. (1988) The many faces of *Lamprologus elongatus.* TFH, Nov. pp: 61-62.

KONINGS, A. (1988) *Lamprologus callipterus* en *Julidochromis elongatus. NVC periodiek*, (Dutch Cichl. Assn.) 14 (2).

KONINGS, A. & DIECKHOFF, H.W. (1992) *Tanganyika secrets.* Cichlid Press, St. Leon-Rot, Germany.

STAATS, F. (1972) *Lamprologus savoryi elongatus,* Trewavas & Poll 1952 (Prinzessin von Burundi). *DCG-Info* (German Cichl. Assn.) Nr. 10; pp: 85-90.

TREWAVAS, E. & POLL, M. (1952) Three new species and two new subspecies of the genus *Lamprologus*, cichlid fishes of Lake Tanganyika. *Bull. Inst. Sc. nat. Belgique.* Vol. 28 (50); pp: 1- 16.

Already almost forgotten —*Neolamprologus niger*

Hans-Joachim Herrmann

Neolamprologus niger was described by Poll in 1956, but under the old generic name *Lamprologus*. It was almost another thirty years before it was first introduced to our aquaria. As is so often the case with new imports the demand exceeded the supply, and as a result extremely high prices were demanded —for both wild caught and tank bred specimens— and, of course, paid by aquarists.

Books published in the mid 1980s contained a few remarks on the species, but there was little or nothing to be learned about it from the aquatic press and society journals; this was a pity, as the aquatic press has a large readership and can thus introduce a species to a wider public. Since then there has been very little mention of *Neolamprologus niger* either in Germany or elsewhere, giving rise to the fear that this species may be consigned to total oblivion and disappear from the aquarium hobby over the next few years, as has already happened in the case of a few other species, not only from Lake Tanganyika. It is especially important at the present time, when the conservation of animals and species is a matter for public concern, that we do not lose sight of fishes which have already been kept in our aquaria —even though more interesting or more beautiful, or even simply "newer", species may have become available in the meantime.

So far *Neolamprologus niger* has been found only in the north of Lake Tanganyika in the vicinity of the town of Uvira (Zaïre), in the north west in Kabimba Bay (Zaïre), and on the east coast at Bulu Puint (Cape Kungwe, Tanzania). Because this species, which has a maximum length of 9 cm, inhabits rocky and stony areas of shore- line

where there are numerous hiding places, and is difficult to find on account of its not very striking adult coloration, it is likely that it occurs at further localities where it has not yet been discovered, especially as it is sometimes found at depths of more than 10 metres.

In the aquarium, and, naturally, in nature as well, *Neolamprologus niger* is territorial in its behaviour. A chosen cave or rock crevice is defended against conspecifics, and weaker individuals are chased away. Sometimes a pair which have previously produced young together on several occasions will find themselves at odds. At such times the fins are spread, the gill covers distended, and frontal threat display, during which the mouths of the two individuals are almost in contact, may lead to actual, and violent, mouthfighting. Such "marital strife" may last for several hours or even days, and only when the situation has been clarified will breeding be resumed. Dominant males of *Neolamprologus niger* may, at least in the aquarium, regard several females as their particular property at any given time. In such cases they are kept very busy defending their territory while the females undertake care of the brood.

The species, which with increasing age loses more and more of its yellow juvenile coloration and becomes browner, is easy to breed; but the number of eggs laid is very small. It often happens that there are only one or two eggs per brood, attached to the side of a cave. As there is normally no intraspecific persecution of tiny fry, and further spawnings take place after only a short inter-

Mouth-fighting between male and female is sometimes necessary to dissipate aggression before the breeding period. Photos Hans-Joachim Herrmann.

A wild-caught male *Neolamprologus niger*.

val, it is common to see different generations of juveniles growing up together in the vicinity of the breeding cave, guarded by the female in particular. But as soon as the young are half grown they are obliged to leave the breeding territory, and, in the aquarium, are chased away to the upper layers of the water; or, if the tank is sufficiently large, they will each occupy a relatively small territory.

Female *N. niger* retain the juvenile yellow coloration much longer than males.

In general a 100 litre aquarium is adequate for both the day-to-day maintenance of *Neolamprologus niger* and for breeding; but it is better, although not absolutely necessary, to use a tank with a bottom area of half a square metre or larger. The species appears to enjoy digging out sand from between the rocks in order to expose new caves. For this reason the aquarist should use a substrate of sand and not stint on well constructed piles of rocks. The water which must always be of good quality (regular water changes, efficient filtration, sensible fish population) should be moderately hard to hard with a pH greater than 7. In addition this interesting species should be fed a varied diet of glassworms and mosquito larvae, *Cyclops*, water fleas, flake food, and large as

well as small brine shrimps.

Neolamprologus niger is an ideal cichlid for aquarium maintenance, and it would be a shame if this species were to be consigned to oblivion before it has become properly known.

References

HERRMANN, H.-J. (1987) *Die Buntbarsche der Alten Welt. Tanganjikasee.* Reimar Hobbing, Essen, Germany.
KONINGS, A. (1988) *Tanganjika Cichliden.* Lake Fish Movies & Verduijn Cichlids. Zevenhuizen, Netherlands.
POLL, M. (1956) Résultats scientif. expl. hydrob. belge au lac Tanganika (1946-1947). *Poissons Cichlidae.* Vol. III, fasc. 5B.

Neolamprologus leleupi (Poll, 1956)

Ad Konings

Neolamprologus leleupi became known to aquarists for the first time in 1958 (Riehl & Baensch, 1985). These first specimens came from the northern part of Zaïre where they were caught by collectors of ornamental fishes usually operating in the jungles of what was then the Belgian Congo. As almost all fishes exported from Zaïre at that time were collected in soft acidic waters, *N. leleupi* was thought to come from such waters as well, and this very highly priced fish was maintained in the purest rainwater a fortunate hobbyist could obtain. Needless to say these specimens died within a few days; the softer and more acidic the water the sooner they died. Now every cichlid fancier knows that fishes from Lake Tanganyika need rather hard and alkaline water.

N. leleupi remained a rare fish in the hobby for quite some years until it was bred in larger numbers in the early seventies. In the mid seventies M. Fainzilber exported *N. leleupi* from the Tanzanian east coast of the lake. This geographical variant was described in 1980 as *Lamprologus leleupi longior* (Staeck, 1980). Much earlier Matthes described another subspecies and named it *L. leleupi melas* (Matthes, 1959) because it was dusky coloured and lacked the bright yellow. This subspecies was found at the same locality as *N. leleupi*, namely the northwestern Zaïrean coast, near Bemba. Later on under water observations revealed that such brown-black individuals are also found on the east coast (near Magambo) sharing the habitat with the yellow subspecies (Walter Dieckhoff, pers. comm.). In 1986 Poll, in his revision of the Tanganyika cichlids, placed the subspecies *melas* in synonymy with *N. leleupi leleupi* and gave the subspecies *longior* the status of a species.

The fact that within one population a dusky coloured as well as a yellow coloured morph is found (polychromatism) is remarkable but not unique among cichlids. Poll (1986) found, after examining fresh specimens of the dark morph, that the yellow pigment of such individuals is obscured by the black pigment. The yellow individuals are thus just lacking the black colour. In Lake Tanganyika polychromatic individuals are also known to occur in

Neolamprologus leleupi photographed at a depth of 23 metres at Cap Tembwe, Zaïre.

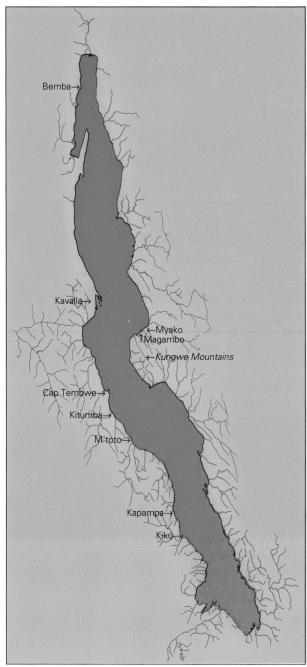

The localities where *N. leleupi* and allied species were found, are indicated.

other species. *Ctenochromis benthicola* has orange as well as brown females (Mireille Schreyen, pers. comm.). Büscher (1991) reports on polychromatism in *N. pectoralis*. Personal observations have revealed that *N. mustax* also shows polychromatism. Cichlids show polychromatism in other water systems as well. In Lake Malawi such individuals are described as orange blotched (OB) or orange (O) and occur in at least 6 species. Among the Cichlasomini in Central America orange individuals are known to occur in several species, e.g. *"Cichlasoma" fenestratum*, *"C." citrinellum*, and *Petenia splendida*.

The yellow *N. leleupi* is thus one morph of a polychromatic species. At several locations it seems that the yellow morph is more frequently seen than the dark one, although *N. leleupi* is a rare species at most locations. Kuwamura (1987), however, reports that *N. leleupi* is common along the central eastern coast near Myako, Tanzania. The dark morph is of course less conspicuous than its yellow counterpart, but it does not seem to occur at all localities where yellow individuals are found. At Cap Tembwe, Zaïre, I observed several yellow individuals of *N. leleupi* but no dark ones. The same is true for two localities south of Cap Tembwe, Kitumba and M'toto. This does not mean that the dark morph is not present in these populations; it just may give an indication of its low abundance.

Some populations of *N. leleupi* (or a very closely related species) do not show yellow pigmented individuals but silvery-beige ones. In these populations one also finds black individuals and light coloured fish. Around Milima, an island of the Kavalla group, I observed a species with a close resemblance to *N. leleupi*. The only obvious morphological difference from known *N. leleupi* appears to be their long

Neolamprologus cf. *leleupi*, a dark morph at Milima Island, Kavalla, Zaïre.

Neolamprologus mustax, a dark morph photographed in Moliro Bay, Zaïre.

A light morph of a *leleupi*-like cichlid at Kapampa, Zaïre.

A dark morph of the same species as photo left. Photographed at Kiku, Zaïre.

pelvic fins. However, in behaviour, polychromatism, and abundance it resembles *N. leleupi*. Again, a very similar population occurs at Kapampa and Kiku. This population lacks the yellow morph but black specimens are found sympatrically with light beige individuals. These cichlids seem to have a higher body than *N. leleupi* from Bemba in the north of the lake. *N. mustax* is closely related to *N. leleupi* and has a higher body. However, at Kiku it was found sympatrically with the *leleupi*-like species.

Nevertheless there is a close relationship between *N. leleupi* and *N. mustax*. *N. leleupi* at M'toto (see photo) has a relatively deep body and, remarkably, a white chin, a feature that was thought to be typical of *N. mustax*. The most northerly known distribution of *N. mustax* is at Kiku which is about 100km south of M'toto. In my personal opinion *N. leleupi* is quite a variable species with a rather broad distribution in Lake Tanganyika. The populations with the yellow colour morph are probably the oldest because these are also found on Tanzanian shores. They were probably present in the paleolakes when the water level was much lower than at present. With the rising water level the main population became split up but remained on the west and east central coasts. The species which has been described as *N. longior* is, from my viewpoint, a population of *N. leleupi*.

The Malagarazi river delta was and still is a

Neolamprologus mustax, the yellow morph, in Moliro Bay, Zaïre.

Neolamprologus leleupi at M'toto has a rather deep body and, remarkably, a white chin.

barrier to the northward expansion of the species on the east coast. There *N. leleupi* is found only south of the river. It is not known whether *N. leleupi* inhabits the rocky shoreline south of the Kungwe mountains. *N. cylindricus*, which is very closely related to *N. leleupi*, is reported from the southern Tanzanian shores of the lake.

On the west coast *N. leleupi* is found in the intermediate and rocky habitats. All individuals observed were solitary and found at depths below 15 metres. *N. leleupi* is a predator feeding mainly on aquatic insects and crustaceans. These are located in the biocover on the rocks or in the cracks between them. A foraging *N. leleupi* covers a large terrain. It is not known if they have a specific feeding territory; also juveniles have been observed feeding on their own. Their solitary behaviour may explain their pugnacious attitude towards conspecifics in aquaria. Only ripe females are tolerated in the male's domain. Eggs, however, are deposited in the female's cave. In the lake a wandering male may therefore find a ripe female in her cave and spawn with her. In the aquarium *N. leleupi* forms a pair during the breeding period.

Breeding pairs have not yet been observed in the lake but it is likely that the male stays with the female until the young are big enough to face the outside world on their own. In the aquarium the pair bond rarely lasts longer than one month.

References

BÜSCHER, H.H. (1991) Ein neuer Tanganjikasee-Cichlide aus Zaire. *DATZ*, 44, pp: 788-792.

KUWAMURA, T. (1987) Distribution of fishes in relation to the depth and substrate at Myako, East-middle Coast of Lake Tanganyika. *Afr. Study Monographs*, 7, pp: 1-14.

MATTHES, H. (1959) Une sous-espèce nouvelle de *Lamprologus leleupi: Lamprologus leleupi melas* ssp. n. (Cichlidae). Fol. Scient. Afr. Centr. V. 1: p: 18.

POLL, M. (1986) Classification des Cichlidae du lac Tanganika: Tribus, genres et espèces. *Mémoires de la classe des sciences. Académie royale de Belgique.* Collection in-8°-2ᵉ série, T. XLV, Fasc. 2.

RIEHL, R. & BAENSCH, H.A. (1985) *Aquarien Atlas. Band 1.* Mergus Verlag, Melle, Germany.

STAECK, W. (1980) Ein neuer Cichlide vom Ostufer des Tanganjikasees, *Lamprologus leleupi longior* n. ssp. (Pisces-Cichlidae). *Rev. Zool. afr.* 94(1): pp: 11-14.

Neolamprologus pectoralis Büscher, 1991

Ad Konings

Neolamprologus pectoralis was recently described by Heinz Büscher (1991). He collected the type material himself on the southwestern coast of Lake Tanganyika, which belongs to Zaïre. The holotype was collected near a village named Tembwe (not to be mistaken with Cap Tembwe); other type material was caught at Kizike, about 70 km south of Moba. Büscher further reports that *N. pectoralis* was observed south of Lunangwa, about 120 km south of Moba, but specimens from this area were not included in the type series.

The name *pectoralis* alludes to the large pectoral fins which are a remarkable and conspicuous feature of this species. The length of the pectoral fin is about the length of the head. This is much larger than in other known lamprologines with a rounded caudal fin. Another feature unknown in any other cichlid is the length of the lower lateral line which extends from a little behind the gill cover to the caudal peduncle. In other cichlids the lower part of the system is much shorter and begins on the rear half of the body. With these two features it is simple to distinguish *N. pectoralis* from other lamprologines. It may be closely related to *N. furcifer*, a cichlid with a similar body shape and long pectoral fins (90% of head length (Poll, 1956)). It is, however, easily distinguished from that species by the rounded caudal fin; that of *N. furcifer* has long filamentous lobes.

In its natural habitat *N. pectoralis* is readily recognised by its large pectorals which are moved slowly but steadily. Especially when seen from above this species gives a very striking impression. Many lamprologines have colourless pectoral fins but those of *N. pectoralis* have a deep colour. There are two colour morphs of this species known, dark brown and yellow, and the pectorals are coloured accordingly. Büscher reports that both colour morphs are present at all three locations given, but that the yellow morph is rare. The yellow colour is seen in juveniles as well as in adult individuals. *N. pectoralis* attains a total length of about 14 cm. Females remain a little smaller than males. The natural habitat of *N. pectoralis* is found in the intermediate habitat although most individuals are found in the proximity of rocks. It maintains close contact with the rocky substrate and moves around the rocks in the same fashion as is seen in *N. furcifer*, i.e. the ventral part of the body remains just a few millimetres above the substrate while the fish follows the contours of the rock.

N. pectoralis is a rather rare cichlid and occurs at depths deeper than 15 metres. Sometimes an adult pair was observed, probably in front of their cave, but most other individuals were solitary sub-adults. Büscher found that pairs occupy horizontal nests which have a very low entrance but which extend deep into the rock (deeper than 60 cm).

The food found in stomachs of some specimens comprise crustaceans, insect larvae, Copepods, snail fragments, algal strands, and sand grains (Büscher, 1991). It seems that *N. pectoralis* is a predator although not specialised.

Some speculations about the large pectoral fins —not so much the size but more the deep colour of the pectorals makes them so conspicuous— were given by Büscher. He

Neolamprologus pectoralis at Tembwe, Zaïre.

A juvenile *N. pectoralis* at Kapampa, Zaïre.

Neolamprologus nigriventris, photographed at Kiku, Zaïre, is probably closely related to *N. pectoralis.*

suggested that on the one hand these fins may give the fish a more acurate control of movement and on the other they may optimise the flow of oxygen-rich water inside the narrow caves they occupy. *N. furcifer* also has large pectoral fins (but weakly coloured) and behaves in a similar way to *N. pectoralis.* So it may indeed be that these fins play a role in the characteristic way these species move about over the substrate. Another feature which has no counterpart among other cichlids is the highly developed lateral line system. It may increase the sensitivity of predator detection, especially in the dark recesses of the habitat, but it also could be an optimised method of prey detection. When observing *N. pectoralis* in its natural environment it was noted that, except for the pectoral fins, it does not move much. The movement of invertebrate prey (crustaceans) may be stimulated by the flow of (oxygen-rich) water. The continuous paddling with the fins may thus arouse invertebrates in the immediate vicinity of the fish. Their movements can be detected by the lateral line system and, thanks to the extension forwards, also

close to the cichlid's head. Other cichlids have highly developed sensory pores on the head with which they detect prey (eg. *Aulonocara*), so maybe *N. pectoralis* developed the other part of the sensory system for prey detection.

At Kiku, just north of the Lunangwa river, I found a species which may be closely related to *N. pectoralis.* It lacks the deep colour in the pectoral fins and is characterised by having black coloration on the lower third of the otherwise beige body. It was recently described as *Neolamprologus nigriventris* by Büscher (1992). It may be found sympatrically with *N. pectoralis* because *N. nigriventris* has been found a few kilometres south of Kapampa close to the area where I photographed *N. pectoralis.*

References

BÜSCHER, H.H. (1991) Ein neuer Tanganjikasee-Cichlide aus Zaire. *DATZ,* 44, pp: 788-792.
BÜSCHER, H.H. (1992) *Neolamprologus nigriventris* n. sp.: Ein neuer Tanganjikasee-Cichlide (Cichlidae, Lamprologini). *DATZ,* 45, pp: 778-783.

Julidochromis ornatus Boulenger, 1898

Ad Konings

The rocky coast at Kapampa. The fish fauna at this locality is, perhaps, one of the most interesting in the lake.

Julidochromis ornatus was described by Boulenger (1898) from a population which inhabits the rocky shores near Mpulungu. This population is characterised by individuals with a white-yellow ground colour, two black horizontal stripes and a black band in the lower part of the dorsal fin. They have been exported under the trade name of "White Ornatus". According to Boulenger's description *J. ornatus* should have 40 to 45 scales in a longitudinal series. This provides a simple character on the basis of which we can distinguish it from *Julidochromis transcriptus* which was described by Matthes in 1959 from a population of the rocky shores of Zaïre, near Bemba. *J. transcriptus*, like all other known species of the genus, has 32 to 36 scales in a longitudinal series. Matthes, in 1962, redescribed *J. ornatus* on the basis of specimens found in the northern part of the lake, and concluded that this species also has 32 to 35 scales, which makes the colour pattern the sole difference between the two species.

In the early eighties Brichard discovered other populations of *Julidochromis* on the Zaïrean coast. Alain Gillot from Zaïre Cichlids (Kalemie) exported some of these variants in 1990. In September 1991 I visited the location, Kapampa-Kileba, where Alain used to collect this species. Here I found a similar situation to that which Brichard describes for *J. transcriptus* in his books. *J. ornatus*, as I would like to identify the species in the photograph, lives in the intermediate habitat and has a considerable depth range. Interestingly, individuals with a dark coloration are found together with those having a much lighter colour pattern. The ones living at greater depths are usually much darker than those in the shallows, but this is not a rule. Dark specimens were also found in shallow water. A few miles on either side of this location we found *J. ornatus* with the more common colour pattern consisting of the three horizontal stripes (see photo page 23).

Brichard (1978) reports that *J. transcriptus* can be found in different populations separated by just a few miles of sandy beach and alternating with populations of *J. ornatus*.

Knowing the great variability *Julidochromis* can show in a single population, and knowing their lake-wide but alternating distribution, one would have to prove that *J. transcriptus* and *J. ornatus* are indeed two different species by finding a locality

A wild caught female *Julidochromis ornatus* from Kapampa-Kileba, Zaïre.

where both species live sympatrically. Such a
locality is not yet known.

A similar situation exists for *J. marlieri* and *J. regani*, i.e. there is no location known where both species are found sympatrically.

For the time being I refer to the Kapampa *Julidochromis* as *J. ornatus* even though they are sold as "Zaïre Transcriptus".

References

BRICHARD, P. (1978) *Fishes of Lake Tanganyika.* TFH Publ. Inc., Neptune, New Jersey.

MATTHES, H. (1962) Poissons nouveaux ou intéressants du lac Tanganika et du Ruanda. *Ann. Mus. r. Afr. Centr. Tervuren* Serie in 8 - Sci. Zool. No 111: 27-88.

Julidochromis ornatus at Kiku, Zaïre.

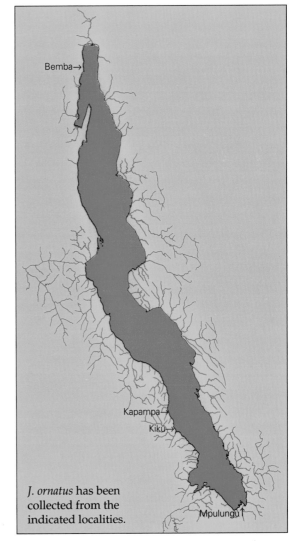

J. ornatus has been collected from the indicated localities.

Speciation, DNA, and *Tropheus*

Ad Konings

In August 1992 Sturmbauer & Meyer published an article in which they claimed to have deduced a phylogenetic tree (a kind of pedigree of populations and species) for *Tropheus* by comparing the sequence of two small pieces of the cichlids' DNA. Although it has received considerable attention in the scientific as well as in the aquaristic press, opinions regarding the acceptability of their findings differ. Persons who have ample experience with the techniques involved largely agree with the authors; persons who are well versed with the cichlids in question find it difficult to accept their ideas. Before I try to explain their results and give my personal ideas about their usefulness, some terms must be defined.

A **phylogenetic tree** is a graphic representation of the descent of populations, species and groups of species. It shows which of these are closely related and how they evolved. A phylogenetic tree shows the evolution of related populations and species from a single ancestor.

Speciation is the evolution of new species and may take place in various ways (Wiley, 1981). A species is rather difficult to define because it is a natural group of individuals which recognise each other as belonging to this group. This definition is useless to us because we don't know whether an individual from population A recognises an individual from population B as being conspecific or not. The species-specific recognition is expressed if and when individuals from population A, under natural circumstances, mate with individuals from B. If interbreeding does not occur we are unable to tell with certainty whether A and B are conspecific or not. When an apparent species consists of several populations which are geographically separated then the assignment of two or more of these populations to one species is the personal opinion of the author.

DNA is the abbreviation for *d*eoxyribo*n*ucleic-*a*cid. The DNA molecule is found mainly in the nucleus of a cell and is responsible for the transmission of hereditary characteristics.

The nucleus of a cell contains **chromosomes**, each of which consists of a single DNA molecule wrapped up in a coat of proteins. Almost all vertebrate organisms have a double set of such chromosomes, one received from the mother and the other from the father. Although the DNA molecules are extremely complex they are built from only four different building blocks. It is the sequence of these blocks (bases) which is very important.

A **gene** is a section of the DNA molecule whose sequence, after decoding, is responsible for a protein. A change to a single building block in the sequence, a **mutation**, may completely abolish the production of the protein; or it may produce a different protein. Most individual mutations, however, have no or only minor effects on the final product. Mutations take place regularly. They are caused mainly by (cosmic) radiation and chemical agents.

Mutations can be present also in the DNA of germ cells (spermatozoid and ovum) and are thus transferred to offspring. These mutations are then added to the gene-pool of the species. A **gene-pool** is the total of all the DNA sequences of all the sexually reproducing individuals of an interbreeding population. Mutations occur continually and when organisms no longer participate in the gene-pool from which they were once derived their DNA sequences gradually deviate from those of the mother gene-pool. It thus follows that not only species but also geographically isolated populations of a single species will have different gene-pools. The variability of a *particular* piece of DNA may be greater between populations of one species than between two sympatric species!

It is self-evident that any mutation which alters a protein so that the organism cannot sustain itself in the community will be selected against; for instance, when a mutation would change the colour of a cichlid from yellow to blue. The blue fish may no longer be recognised by its conspecifics and therefore be excluded from reproduction. This means that its genes are lost from the gene-pool. Thus although mutations occur (almost) randomly in the DNA they do not all become fixed in the gene-pool of the species. There is selection against certain mutations in certain genes. It must be stressed that not all mutations in a gene produce an altered protein and even if a protein is altered there is not necessarily any selection against it (there are several polymorphic populations known among cichlids). Using certain techniques, termed **DNA sequencing**, the sequence of a piece of DNA can be resolved into its individual building blocks. The corresponding piece of DNA from other species can likewise be sequenced and compared. It is erroneous to conclude that differences in the

DNA sequences found during such comparisons are derived solely from the fact that DNAs from different species are being compared: speciation and the continuously occurring mutations are two different processes. Speciation could not occur without genetic variability (caused by mutations) but mutation does not necessarily result in speciation. One million mutations might not make a new species whereas a single mutation in the right gene might.

Sturmbauer & Meyer (1992) deduced their phylogenetic tree from the **number** of mutations in a small section of a gene of the various *Tropheus* populations compared with that of *Oreochromis tanganicae*. (They sequenced a part of the cytochrome b gene and a control region on the mitochondrial DNA.) As has been discussed above the number of mutations says little about

Tropheus sp. "Black" from Bulu Point, Tanzania. This race is also known as the "Kirschfleck Moorii".

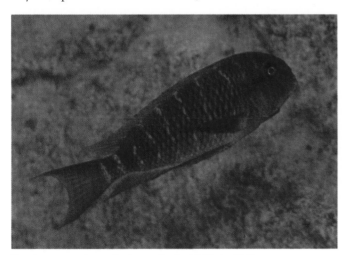

Tropheus annectens photographed at M'toto, Zaïre.

This race of *T. annectens* is known as *T. polli*; it is found near Bulu Point, Tanzania. According to Sturmbauer & Meyer this population is more closely related to the "Kirschfleck Moorii" than to *T. annectens* from Zaïre!

speciation (because it is not a continuous process). However, owing to the fact that mutations occur continually, it may indicate the age of a particular gene. The more differences one finds between two genepools the longer these pools have been separated. Sturmbauer & Meyer remarked: "The morphology of 'living fossils', like horse-shoe crabs, has remained essentially unchanged for millions of years, although these organisms exhibit normal levels of molecular evolution." These authors thus note that mutations (molecular evolution) do occur but that the horse-shoe crab still looks like it did a hundred million years ago. And, as I would understand their remark, the present-day hors-shoe crab is still the same species as it was hundred million years ago. DNA sequencers compare numbers of mutations and thus look at the length of the period during which different populations (genepools) have been isolated.

On the basis of their sequencing data Sturmbauer & Meyer cannot realistically say much about speciation among *Tropheus* and thus cannot give a true phylogenetic tree. However, their investigations do suggest that the populations of the *Tropheus* species are likely to be old, much older than the species in Lake Malawi and Lake Victoria.

In my opinion the discovery of the antiquity of the *Tropheus* species is very interesting and deserves more attention than the proposed new classification based on the number of DNA mutations.

There are a few other points in the publication that need to be discussed. First is the material used in the comparisons. Owing to the fact that it is virtually impossible to extract DNA from formalin-fixed fishes DNA sequencers need fresh material or fishes that have been fixed in alcohol. Sturmbauer & Meyer obtained most of their fresh material from Laif DeMason (Old World Exotic Fish in Florida) who, in turn, imported it from several stations in Africa. Among the fishes used there were also some bred in ponds in Burundi which are thus derived from a limited number of females. When comparing individuals from the same pond one expects to find very little difference between the DNAs. This is likely to be true in the case of the group of 10 individuals of the Bemba variant eight of which were identical. The other group used in the comparisons stemmed from Mpulungu and consisted of wild caught specimens (DeMason, pers. comm.). The natural variation among these ten fishes was demonstrated by the finding

According to Sturmbauer & Meyer this race of *Tropheus* sp. "Black" from Bemba is more closely related to *T. brichardi* from Nyanza-Lac (the "Choco Moorii") than to *Tropheus* sp. "Black" from Kiriza!

Tropheus sp. "Black" from Kiriza, Zaïre.

Tropheus brichardi from Nyanza Lac, Burundi.

that eight out of ten individuals appeared to be different for the gene tested.

The part of the paper that really disturbed me was the assumption that the "Kirschfleck" or "Double Spot Moorii" was the species most closely related to *T. polli*! I regard, on grounds of coloration, morphology, distribution, and behaviour, *T. polli* as a population of *T. annectens* but Sturmbauer & Meyer found more mutations between these two populations than between *T. polli* and the "Kirschfleck". As mentioned before, the number of mutations has little effect on speciation, as is nicely demonstrated by these comparisons. What the results may suggest is that the sections of DNA tested of the "Kirschfleck Moorii" and *T. polli* are of similar antiquity but not that these species are closely related (within *Tropheus*). Personally I feel that the composition of a small fraction of DNA from the two samples of each species used should not be given the importance inferred by Sturmbauer & Meyer. Not only the "Kirschfleck" and *T. polli* were regarded as closely related (within the genus) but also the "Bemba" or "Orange Moorii" and *T. brichardi* from Nyanza! *T. brichardi* from Kavalla, according to these authors, finds its most closely related populations at Mpulungu, Kala, and Kasanga! For DNA-scientists this may sound irrelevant but for aquarists well versed with these species it sounds ridiculous.

The crux of the matter is that the variability of a DNA section can be greater in two populations of a single species than in two sympatric species. It is not the *number* of mutations that make a species but *where* in the genes such mutations have occurred.

Acknowledgement

I thank Dr. Irv Kornfield, who, although not sharing my views, critically read the manuscript and gave valuable comments.

References

STURMBAUER, C & MEYER, A. (1992) Genetic divergence, speciation and morphological stasis in a lineage of African cichlid fishes. *Nature*, vol. 358: pp 578-581.

WILEY, E.O. (1981) *Phylogenetics: the theory and practice of phylogenetic systematics*. John Wiley & Sons, New York.

Bemba

Kiriza

Nyanza Lac

"T. polli"
"Kirschfleck"

M'toto

■ = *Tropheus* sp. "Black"
□ = *Tropheus duboisi*
■ = *Tropheus brichardi*
■ = *Tropheus annectens*
□ = *Tropheus moorii*
■ = *Tropheus* sp. "Red"

MALAWIAN CICHLIDS

A revision of the genus *Sciaenochromis* Eccles & Trewavas, 1989 (Pisces, Cichlidae)

Ad Konings

Abstract

The type species of the cichlid genus *Sciaenochromis* is *Haplochromis serranoides* Ahl, 1927, renamed *H. ahli* (Trewavas, 1935) because of homonymy. Re-examination of the holotype in Berlin and rediscovery of the species in Lake Malawi show that *S. ahli* is not the species so identified by Trewavas (1935) and by Eccles & Trewavas (1989). *S. ahli* is here redescribed and the genus *Sciaenochromis* is redefined and is limited to its type species and three related species, here named and described as new to science.

In 1989 David Eccles and Ethelwynn Trewavas defined many new genera in their revision of the non-mbuna haplochromines of Lake Malawi. The diagnoses of most of these genera were primarily based on the melanin pattern of juveniles and mature females. This in *Sciaenochromis* was stated to include an oblique series of spots.

The type species of Sciaenochromis Eccles & Trewavas is *Haplochromis serranoides* Ahl, 1927, renamed *H. ahli* by Trewavas, 1935, because the name *H. serranoides* had already been used by Regan for a species of Lake Victoria. Although both species are now placed in different genera *H. serranoides* Ahl is a primary junior homonym and must be rejected. Both authors were struck by the general resemblance between their species and fishes of the marine genus *Serranus*.

Ahl based his species on a single specimen, the holotype, collected by Professor Fülleborn near Alt Langenburg on the northeastern shore of Lake Nyasa (Malawi). Alt Langenburg is the site of an old wooden church in the north of the lake (Hans-J. Paepke, pers. comm.; see map). The holotype is preserved in the Zoological Museum of the Humboldt University in Berlin, Germany (registration number 22708) and was re-examined by me in October 1992 in Berlin.

S. ahli has recently been rediscovered in the northern part of the lake and Saulos Mwale of Salima, Malawi, was successful in catching two specimens, which have been used in this study. These and the re-examined holotype have shown that the common concept of the species and consequently of the genus, of which it is the type species, is incorrect. The definition of *Sciaenochromis* as given by Eccles and Trewavas includes the statement "...melanin pattern consisting of an oblique series of spots, usually also with traces of the vertical component of the pleisiomorphic pattern." There is no trace of an oblique series of spots in either the holotype or the freshly caught specimens. Transverse (vertical) bars are present, either expressed or facultative, in almost all haplochromines and other cichlids. Since Eccles & Trewavas give primary importance to the melanin pattern in defining genera, both the definition and the contained species of *Sciaenochromis* must be changed to agree with the changed concept of the type species.

Pending further study, the two species placed with *S. ahli* in *Sciaenochromis* by Eccles & Trewavas are now assigned to *Mylochromis* (senior synonym of *Maravichromis*; see Derijst & Snoeks, 1992) where both '*S.*' *gracilis* and '*S.*' *spilostichus* seem to be related to *M. formosus*.

With *S. ahli* in the newly defined genus *Sciaenochromis* are now included three species new to science.

A cichlid usually referred to as *Haplochromis ahli* has been known to aquarists since 1979. This fish was first imported in 1972 (Cooney, 1979) as the

A freshly caught male of *Sciaenochromis ahli* at Mdoka, Malawi.

Electric Blue Haplochromis and has subsequently been known as *Haplochromis jacksoni* (eg. Axelrod & Burgess, 1979) or as *Haplochromis ahli* (eg. Cooney, 1979). This species, which is now well established in the aquaristic hobby and which is bred in captivity in large quantities, is described in this work as a species new to science.

The measurements were taken in accordance with Barel *et al.* (1977), except for the depth of the preorbital bone, which is the length of a line practically bisecting the lacrimal (Trewavas, 1935; Eccles & Trewavas, 1989: 20, fig. 3).

Sciaenochromis Eccles & Trewavas

Diagnosis

Predatory haplochromines endemic to Lake Malawi with the mouth slightly oblique. Lower jaw strong, with the symphysis almost perpendicular to the dental plane. Teeth in 3 or 4 series, outermost simple or with a very slight shoulder, not closely crowded, but spaces between outer teeth less than tooth diameter. Premaxillary pedicel 3.9 to 5.2 times in head length. Lower pharyngeal bone with small compressed teeth. 9 to 11 gill-rakers on lower part of anterior arch.

The melanin pattern consists of 9 to 12 vertical

bars of a width varying between one and three scales. The bars are permanently visible although weak in some live individuals. Under certain circumstances one or two vertical bands may have a deeper coloured centre which appears as a spot. Such spots, however, do not, in the material examined, definitively indicate a suppressed longitudinal element, either diagonal or horizontal.

The statement in the former generic diagnosis that an oblique series of spots is present was probably due to the inclusion in *S. ahli* of specimens now excluded.

Stigmatochromis is seen as the species group with the closest relation to *Sciaenochromis*. Species of the genus *Stigmatochromis* are distinguished from those of *Sciaenochromis* by their melanin pattern consisting of three spots on the flank, by having a longer premaxillary pedicel (3.0 to 3.5 times in head length in *Stigmatochromis* and 3.9 to 5.2 times in *Sciaenochromis*), and by the wider spaced setting of the outer teeth on the jaws.

Key to the species of *Sciaenochromis*

1. Interorbital width more than 6.8 times in head length. .... *S. psammophilus*

   Interorbital width 4.8 to 5.9 times in head length 2

2. Premaxillary pedicel less than 4.2 times in head length .... *S. fryeri*

   Premaxillary pedicel 5.1 to 5.2 times in head length 3

3. Caudal peduncle 6.1 to 6.3 times in standard length, caudal peduncle depth 1.2 to 1.5 times in its length; depth of preorbital bone 5.9 to 6.4 times in head length. .... *S. ahli*

   Caudal peduncle 5.4 times in standard length; depth of caudal peduncle 1.7 times in its length, depth of preorbital bone 8.3 times in head length. .... *S. benthicola*

Sciaenochromis ahli (Trewavas, 1935)

Haplochromis serranoides (*non* Regan) Ahl, 1927: 54
Haplochromis ahli Trewavas, 1935: 101; (holotype only); Jackson, 1961: 571.

Derivation of name

Named after Dr. Ernst Ahl, Zoological Museum of the Humboldt University, Berlin, who, in 1927, described this species as *Haplochromis serranoides* from a specimen collected by Dr. Fülleborn.

Diagnosis

A cichlid of moderate size, attaining about 170mm SL, with the melanin pattern showing 10 to 11 vertical bars. The head profile from the start of the dorsal fin to the tip of the snout is slightly convex. The lower profile of the head is straight and almost horizontal. Differs from *S. psammophilus* in having a larger interorbital width, 4.8 to 5.9 as opposed to 6.8 to 7.7 times in head length; from *S. fryeri* in having a shorter premaxillary pedicel, 5.1 to 5.2 as opposed to 3.9 to 4.2 times in head length, and from *S. benthicola* by having a deeper preorbital bone, 5.9 to 6.4 as opposed to 8.3 times in head length, and by having a shorter caudal peduncle, 6.1 to 6.3 as opposed to 5.4 times in standard length.

Description

Depth of body 2.8 to 2.9, head length 3.0 to 3.2 times in standard length. Snout 3.1 to 3.2, eye diameter 3.2 to 3.4, interorbital width 4.8 to 5.9, lower jaw 2.2 to 2.4, premaxillary pedicel 5.1 to 5.2, and preorbital depth 5.9 to 6.4 times in head length. Depth of preorbital bone 1.9 to 2.0 times in snout length. Lower jaw projecting with a pronounced mental knob; maxilla extending between verticals from anterior edge and centre of eye. Teeth in 3 to 4 series, unicuspid. Lower pharyngeal bone with thin bicuspid teeth. 10 to 11 gill-rakers on the lower part of the anterior arch. Lower 4 rakers reduced, merely knob-shaped; others slender, simple or with slightly forked tips.
4 or 5 series of scales on the cheek, 33 or 34 in a longitudinal series.
Dorsal fin XVI-XVII 9-11. Anal fin III 9-10. Pectoral fin 2.9 to 3.2 times in standard length, 1.0 to 1.1 times in head length.
Caudal peduncle 6.1 to 6.3 times in standard length, peduncle depth 1.2 to 1.5 times in its length.

Material examined

Holotype: (*H. serranoides*) Zoological Museum Berlin, No. 22708, female, 160 mm standard length; Alt Langenburg, Tanzania, collected by Fülleborn. Remark: Ahl gives the total length as 195 mm. A standard length of 168 mm and a total length of 197 mm was given by Eccles & Trewavas (1989). On 13th Oct. 1992 the holotype had a standard length of 160 mm and a total length of 187 mm.

Other material: Royal Museum for Central Africa, Tervuren, Nos. 92.146.P.1-2. Male, 130.5 mm standard length; female 126.8 mm standard length; Mdoka, Malawi, collected 26-11-1990 by S. Mwale.

Distribution

The holotype was caught in the northeastern part of the lake, which belongs to Tanzania. The two additional specimens originate from Mdoka in the northwestern part. At Chewere specimens with a great similarity to those at Mdoka were seen and photographed. A photograph taken at Taiwan Reef, about 10 km north of Chizumulu Island, may show *S. ahli* but the fish was not collected for confirmation (see photo). It was found in a rocky habitat, not a common biotope for this species.

Ecology

S. ahli was found at three different locations over sand in the vicinity of rocks. A single specimen was observed in a purely rocky habitat. At Mdoka a male in breeding coloration was collected at the end of

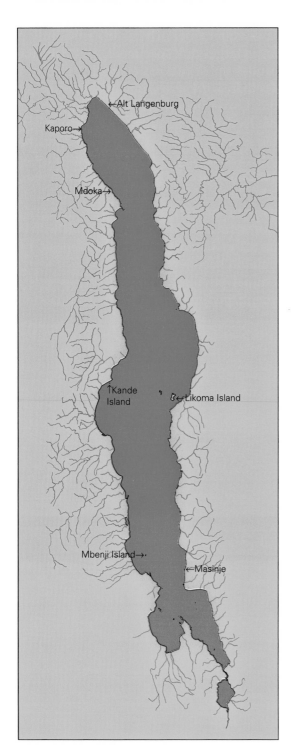

Map of Lake Malawi.

Sciaenochromis fryeri sp. nov.

Cyrtocara ahli: Hacard & Hacard, 1989: p17; Kotschetow, 1989: p207; Kowite, 1988: p10; Mayland, 1982a: p140; Mayland, 1982b: p43.
Haplochromis ahli: Allgayer, 1985: fiche technique; Axelrod & Burgess, 1986: p354; Cooney, 1979: p5; Folcke, 1987: p91; Kapralski, 1988: p32; Loiselle, 1979: p45; Loiselle, 1985: p18; Riehl & Baensch, 1989: p769; Staeck, 1985: p203; Staeck, 1988: p110.
Haplochromis cf. *ahli*: Staeck, 1983: p248.
Sciaenochromis ahli: Konings, 1989: p179; Konings, 1990: p104; Mayland, 1990: p148.
Haplochromis jacksoni: Axelrod & Burgess, 1979: p229.

This species is well known among aquarists as "Haplochromis Electric Blue".

Derivation of name

Named after Dr. Geoffrey Fryer, former Fisheries Research Officer of the Joint Fisheries Research Organisation stationed in Nkhata Bay, who systematically observed the fishes of Lake Malawi in their natural habitat.

S. cf. *ahli*. This specimen, photographed at Taiwan Reef, was not collected for proper identification. The preferred habitat of S. ahli seems to be the sandy regions. At the reef it may have adapted to the purely rocky situation.

S. ahli, a female at Mdoka at a depth of about 25 m.

November 1990 (see photo) but such males have not been observed under water. Therefore details about breeding behaviour cannot be given. Saulos Mwale, who collected these specimens, told me that the male has a small nest on the sand. No further details have been recorded. Females and non-breeding males are frequently observed over the sand, but only during this (breeding?) period. *S. ahli* could not be found at Mdoka (or anywhere else) during visits in May 1989 and in August 1992. Although *S. ahli* has not been observed hunting it is likely to be a piscivorous cichlid.

Diagnosis

A cichlid of small to medium size, attaining about 115 mm standard length, with the melanin pattern showing 9 to 12 vertical bars. The dorsal head profile is convex. The basal head profile is straight and almost horizontal. Differs from the other species in the genus by the dark coloration, also seen in females. Differs from *S. ahli* by having a longer premaxillary pedicel, 3.9 to 4.2 as opposed to 5.1 to 5.2 times in head length; differs from *S. psammophilus* by having a larger interorbital width, 4.9 to 5.7 as opposed to 6.8 to 7.7 times in head length; differs from *S. benthicola* in having a longer premaxillary pedicel, 3.9 to 4.2 as opposed to 5.2 times in head length, and by having a shorter and deeper caudal peduncle (length/depth ratio 1.3 to 1.4 as opposed to 1.7 in *S. benthicola*).

Description

Depth of body 3.0 to 3.5, head length 2.9 to 3.1 times in standard length. Snout 2.8 to 3.4, eye diameter 2.9 to 3,4, interorbital width 4.9 to 5.7, lower jaw 2.2 to 2.4, premaxillary pedicel 3.9 to 4.2, and preorbital depth 5.3 to 6.6 times in head length. Preorbital depth 1.7 to 1.9 times in snout length.

Jaws equal anteriorly, or lower slightly projecting in large adult specimens, with a mental knob; caudal tip of maxilla extending below the iris. Teeth in 3 or 4 series, unicuspid or weakly bicuspid. Lower pharyngeal bone with slender bicuspid teeth. 10 to 11 gill-rakers on the lower part of the anterior arch. Lower 3 to 4 rakers reduced; others short and stout with flattened shape, upper rakers usually bifid sometimes trifid.

5 to 6 series of scales on the cheek, 32 to 33 in a longitudinal series.

Dorsal fin XV-XVI 9-11. Anal fin III 8-10. Pectoral fin 3.2 to 3.7 times in standard length, 1.0 to 1.3 times in head length.

Caudal peduncle 5.8 to 6.3 times in standard length, peduncle depth 1.3 to 1.4 times in length.

A female *Sciaenochromis fryeri*, an aquarium specimen of unknown origin.

Sciaenochromis fryeri, a male in its natural habitat. Photographed at Mbenji Island.

Holotype: Royal Museum for Central Africa, Tervuren, No. 92.146.P.4. Male, 113.2 mm standard length (total length 141.5 mm); Mbenji Island, Malawi, collected 16-11-1989 by S. Mwale.

Paratypes: British Museum (Natural History), London, No. 1956.6.4.10. Male, 107.7 mm standard length (132.6 mm total length); Nkhata Bay, Malawi, collected by G. Fryer (JFRO).
BM(NH), London, No. 1988. 1.22.29. Male, 96.1 mm standard length (121.8 mm total length); Cape Maclear, Malawi, collected by J. Trendall and E. Trewavas (Fisheries Monkey Bay) on 25-04-1985.
Royal Museum for Central Africa, Tervuren, Nos. 92.146.P.5-7. Males, 68.9, 76.3, and 78.8 mm standard length (86.5, 95.6, and 98.4 mm total length); Likoma Island, Malawi, collected by S.M. Grant on 29-07-1992.

Distribution

S. fryeri is found throughout Lake Malawi. It was observed on almost all rocky coast along the lake including remote islets and reefs such as Taiwan Reef, Chinyankwazi and Chinyamwezi Islands. It has been collected on the Tanzanian coast (Laif DeMason, pers. comm.).

Ecology

The preferred habitat of *S. fryeri* is the rocky and intermediate habitat. It is rarely found over sand, and when it is then not far from a rocky substrate. It has never been observed in pairs or small groups. *S. fryeri*, a piscivore, roams through the habitat on its own and is seen infrequently at depths between 10 and 40 metres. It may be classified as a rare cichlid, though in the period between November and March it is commonly found close to nests of *Bagrus meridionalis* (Kampango). Here it hunts juvenile *Copadichromis* released above the nest of the breeding catfish forming so-called "selfish schools" (McKaye & Oliver, 1980). During other periods of the year it hunts mainly small cichlids from the genera *Copadichromis* and *Protomelas*, which are regularly found among the rocks.
Adult males permanently show their azure-blue coloration, including when hunting, which makes them very conspicuous. Females have a dark brown colour and are rarely seen. In more than 300 hours of diving, I was able to observe only three females, one of which was mouthbrooding. The female coloration blends well into the shadows of the recesses in the rocky substrate. They may hunt in a different part of the habitat and rarely venture out into the open. Breeding has not been observed in the lake but aquarium observations indicate that spawning can take place at any suitable site. A nest is not constructed. A territory is defended only while spawning lasts.
Large males usually attain a whitish blue colour on the dorsal part of the head.

Sciaenochromis psammophilus sp. nov.

Sciaenochromis ahli (part): Eccles & Trewavas, 1989: p232 (fig. 133?).
This species has been exported under the trade name "Electric Blue Kande" and has been referred to in aquaristic literature as *Sciaenochromis* sp. "Blue Kande" (Konings, 1989: p 179, 1990: p158) and as *Sciaenochromis* sp. "Sand" (Konings, 1990: p225).

Derivation of name

The name refers to the fact that this species is normally found over sandy substrates. (Greek: psammos=sand; philos=loving).

Diagnosis

A cichlid of small to medium size, attaining about 116 mm standard length, with the melanin pattern showing 9 to 11 vertical bars. The dorsal head profile is convex. The lower head profile is straight and almost horizontal. Differs from the other three species in having a smaller interorbital width which is 6.8 to 7.7 times in head length; the interorbital width in *S. ahli* is 4.8 to 5.9, in *S. fryeri* 4.9 to 5.7, and in *S. benthicola* 5.2 times in head length.

Description

Depth of body 3.1 to 3.4, head length 2.9 to 3.0 times in standard length. Snout 3.3 to 3.4, eye diameter 3.2 to 3.9, interorbital width 6.8 to 7.7, lower jaw 2.3 to 2.5, premaxillary pedicel 4.3 to 5.1, and preorbital depth 6.0 to 7.0 times in head length. Preorbital depth 1.8 to 2.0 times in snout length.
Jaws equal anteriorly, or lower slightly projecting in large adult specimens, with a mental knob; caudal tip of maxilla extending below the iris.

A male *Sciaenochromis psammophilus* photographed at the type locality, Kande Island.

A breeding male *S. psammophilus* defending its cave-crater nest. Kande Island, Malawi.

Teeth in 3 or 4 series, unicuspid or weakly bicuspid. Lower pharyngeal bone with slender bicuspid teeth. 10 to 11 gill-rakers on the lower part of the anterior arch. Lower 3 to 4 rakers reduced; others slender and simple.

5 to 7 series of scales on the cheek, 31 to 32 in a longitudinal series.

Dorsal fin XV-XVI 8-10. Anal fin III 8-9. Pectoral fin 3.0 to 3.5 times in standard length, 1.0 to 1.2 times in head length.

Caudal peduncle 5.5 to 6.3 times in standard length, peduncle depth 1.5 to 1.6 times in its length.

Material examined

Holotype: Royal Museum for Central Africa, Tervuren, No. 92.146.P.8. Male, 98.6 mm standard length (123.6 mm total length); Kande Island, Malawi; collected on 03-12-1990 by S. Mwale.
Paratype: Royal Museum for Central Africa, Tervuren, No. 92.146.P.9. Female, 99.5 mm standard length (123.6 mm total

Sciaenochromis psammophilus in its natural habitat at Masinje, Malawi.

length); same collection data as holotype.

Other material: BM(NH), London, No. 1935.6.14. 1474. Unsexed, 110.9 mm standard length (140 mm total length); Vua, coll. C. Christy.

BM(NH), London, No. 1935. 6.14.1460-68 (nr. 2737). Male, 115.3 mm standard length (143.1 mm total length); South-East arm of the lake. Coll. C. Christy.

BM(NH), London, No. 1935. 6.14.1469-71 (left half of lower jaw missing). Unsexed, 103.3 mm standard length (128.4 mm total length); South-East arm of the lake. Coll. C. Christy.

Distribution

Around Kande Island, in the central western part of the lake which borders on an approximately 150 km-long sandy shore. *S. psammophilus* is commonly observed all year round (Stuart Grant, pers. comm.). Apart from the localities where the material examined was collected, *S. psammophilus* (or at least cichlids with a close resemblance to this species) was also observed at Likoma Island, Masinje, Senga Bay, and Mdoka.

Ecology

S. psammophilus prefers the sandy substrates of the lake. It is seen mostly at a depth of between 5 and 30 metres. It is normally not a common species; only around Kande Island are breeding individuals common throughout the year. Apart from the situation around Kande Island, *S. psammophilus* is a solitary hunter which swims about 30 cm above the sand searching for small, sand-dwelling prey. It has been observed hunting small cichlids, but invertebrates are likely to be taken as well.

Breeding males are territorial and defend an area about 2 metres in diameter. The centre of the territory is a nest excavated in the sand, partly under a rock, creating a so-called cave-crater nest (see photo). When more breeding males are present than suitable rocks nests are also constructed on the open sand. These are very shallow and probably used only to bridge a period of temporary shortage of spawning sites. Males guarding such sites do not seem to have the same intense breeding colours as males defending a cave-crater nest.

Sciaenochromis benthicola sp. nov.

Derivation of name

Refers to the depth at which this species occurs. This species was not observed while scuba div-ing. The single specimen was caught at a great depth with hook and line (Greek: benthos=deep; Latin: cola=dweller).

Diagnosis

A cichlid of small to medium size, the single specimen having a standard length of 118 mm. The melanin pattern shows 12 vertical bars of which, in the freshly caught specimen, the 5th and 9th bar are more intensely coloured than the others. In the preserved state it shows an intensification of the 9th and the 12th bar which appear as a spot. The dorsal head profile is convex. The lower head profile is straight and almost horizontal. Differs from *S. psammophilus* in having a larger interorbital width (5.2 as opposed to 6.8 to 7.7 times in head length). Differs from *S. fryeri* in having a shorter premaxillary pedicel, 5.2 as opposed to 3.9 to 4.2 times in head length, and a smaller preorbital depth, 8.3 as opposed to 5.3 to 6.6 times in head length. Differs from *S. ahli* in having a smaller preorbital depth (8.3 as opposed to 5.9 to 6.4 times in head length) and by having a longer caudal peduncle, 5.4 as opposed to 6.1 to 6.3 times in standard length.

Description

Depth of body 3.3, head length 2.9 times in standard length. Snout 3.4, eye diameter 3.2, interorbital width 5.2, lower jaw 2.2, premaxillary pedicel 5.2, and preorbital depth 8.3 times in head length. Preorbital depth 2.4 times in snout length.

Jaws equal anteriorly with a small mental knob; caudal tip of maxilla extending below the eye. Teeth in 3 series, unicuspid and weakly bicuspid. Lower pharyngeal bone with slender bicuspid teeth. 11 gill-rakers on the lower part of the anterior arch. All rakers are slender and simple, including the lower ones.

5 series of scales on the cheek, 35 in a longitudinal series.

Dorsal fin XVII 10. Anal fin III 9. Pectoral fin 3.1 times in standard length, 1.1 times in head length. Caudal peduncle 5.45 times in standard length, peduncle depth 1.7 times in its length.

Material examined

Holotype: Royal Museum for Central Africa, Tervuren, No. 92.146.P.3. Unsexed, 117.5 mm standard length (144.2 mm total length); Kaporo, Malawi; collected on 29-05-1989.

S. benthicola: holotype. This specimen was collected by hook and line at a great depth.

S. benthicola: holotype in the preserved state.

The stomach is everted into the buccal cavity owing to the rapid drop in pressure when hauled to the surface.

Distribution and ecology

Only one specimen known, from Kaporo.

Acknowledgements

I would like to thank Dr. Ethelwynn Trewavas for her many supportive suggestions and Mr. Martin Geerts and Ms. Mary Bailey for critically reading the manuscript. The assistance of Mr. Stuart Grant and Mr. Saulos Mwale of Salima was of primary importance and is gratefully acknowledged. I further thank Mr. Gordon Howes of the Natural History Museum in London and Dr. Hans-Joachim Paepke of the Zoological Museum in Berlin for their support.

References

AHL, E. (1927) Einige neue Fische der Familie Cichlidae aus dem Nyasa-See. *Sitz. Geselsch. Naturf. Freunde*, No. 1-10, pp 51-62.

ALLGAYER, R. (1985) *Aulonocara baenschi* Meyer & Riehl, 1985 and «*Haplochromis*» *ahli* Trewavas, 1935. *Rev. fr. Cichlid.*, 56: fiches techniques.

AXELROD, H.R. & BURGESS, W.E. (1979) *African cichlids of lakes Malawi and Tanganyika*. 8th Ed. TFH Publ., Neptune NJ, USA.

AXELROD, H.R. & BURGESS, W.E. (1986) *African cichlids of lakes Malawi and Tanganyika*. 11th Ed. TFH Publ., Neptune NJ, USA.

BAREL, C.D.N., Van OIJEN, M.J.P., WITTE, F & WITTE-MAAS, E.L.M. (1977) An introduction to the taxonomy and morphology of the haplochromine cichlidae from Lake Victoria. A manual to Greenwood's revision papers. *Neth. J. Zool.*, 27 (4): pp 333- 389.

COONEY, P. (1979) Breeding the "Electric Blue" Haplochromis. *Buntb. Bull. (Amer. Cichl. Assn.)*. # 75, pp 5-10.

DERIJST, E & SNOEKS, J. (1992) *Maravichromis* Eccles and Trewavas, 1989, a junior synonym of *Mylochromis* Regan, 1920 (Teleostei, Cichlidae). *Cybium* 16 (2): p 173.

ECCLES, D.H. & TREWAVAS. E. (1989) *Malawian cichlid fishes. The classification of some haplochromine genera*. Lake Fish Movies, Herten, Germany.

FOLCKE, M. (1987) "*Haplochromis*" *ahli*. *Cichlidae (Belg. Cichl. Assn.)* 13 (4): pp 91-93.

HACARD, J.P. & HACARD, B. (1989) *Cyrtocara ahli*, le saphir du Malawi. *Aquarium Mag.* 39: p 17-21.

KAPRALSKI, A. (1988) A systematic approach to keeping and breeding African mouthbrooders. *TFH* 37(2): pp 26-34.

KONINGS, A. (1989) *Malawi cichlids in their natural habitat.* Verduijn Cichlids & Lake Fish Movies, Zevenhuizen, Netherlands.

KONINGS, A. (1990) *Cichlids and all the other fishes of Lake Malawi*. TFH Publ., Neptune NJ, USA.

KOTSCHETOW, A.M. (1989) *Exotic fishes*. Lesnaia Promitslennosti, Moscow, Russia.

KOWITE, W.J. (1988) The electric blue Haplochromis. *TFH* 36(7): pp 10-14.

LOISELLE, P.V. (1979) An aquarist's overview of the genus *Haplochromis*. Part 2. The Malawian species. *FAMA*, 2(1): pp 42- 47, pp 78-83.

LOISELLE, P.V. (1985) *The Cichlid Aquarium*. Tetra Press, Melle, Germany.

MAYLAND, H.J. (1982a) *Der Malawi-See und seine Fische*. Landbuch, Hannover, Germany.

MAYLAND, H.J. (1982b) *Buntbarsche des Malawi-Sees*. A. Philler Verlag, Minden, Germany.

MAYLAND, H.J. (1990) *Bewährte und begehrte Cichliden Afrikas*. Landbuch, Hannover, Germany.

McKAYE, K.R. & OLIVER, M.K. (1980) Geometry of a selfish school: defence of cichlid young by bagrid catfish in Lake Malawi, Africa. *Anim. Behav.* 28: p 1287.

RIEHL, R & BAENSCH, H.A. (1989) *Aquarien atlas. Band 3.* Mergus, Melle, Germany.

STAECK, W. (1983) *Cichliden. Entdeckungen und Neuimporte. Band III.* E. Pfriem Verlag, Wuppertal, Germany.

STAECK, W. (1985) Selten gepflegt: der Azurcichlide («*Haplochromis*» *ahli* Trewavas, 1935) aus dem Malawisee. *DATZ*, 38(5): pp 203-205.

STAECK, W. (1988) *Cichliden; Malawi-See*. E. Pfriem Verlag, Wuppertal, Germany.

TREWAVAS, E. (1935) A synopsis of the cichlid fishes of Lake Nyasa. *Ann. Mag. nat. Hist.* (10), 16: pp 65-118.

Similar species found on opposite coastlines in northern Lake Malawi —more clues to a step-wise speciation?

Laif DeMason

Over the last few years, exploration and exports of cichlid species from the previously unknown Tanzanian coast have been undertaken. While many completely new varieties are now known (DeMason, 1992), several species found on the Tanzanian (eastern) shores bear almost identical coloration and form to species already known from the Malawian (western) coastline. These "sister" species' similarities are remarkable as many of these similar populations are separated by 100 km across the deepest portion (700 m) of Lake Malawi! Furthermore several "identical" species are not found directly east-west as latitudinal lines are drawn, but instead geographical populations are consistently skewed along a northeast-southwest axis. In this article, space permits the discussion of some rock-associated mbuna species of the genera *Pseudotropheus*, *Labeotropheus*, and *Cynotilapia*. Similarities can also be found in many non-mbuna species. Furthermore, similarities described here are only gross observations of male coloration and form; nothing is conjectured with respect to dentition and morphometric characteristics.

While many mbuna species in the northern half of Lake Malawi are uniquely different, other species show striking similarities. The genus *Pseudotropheus* is well represented on both the northeastern Tanzanian and the northwestern Malawian coastlines. In Tanzania, yellow morphs of species of the *P. tropheops* complex (traded as "Macrophthalmus") are well represented from Matema to south of Cape Kaiser. Of particular note is the brilliantly-coloured "Macrophthalmus Bright Yellow" found 10 km south of Matema, where rocky habitat begins at Ikombe, Tanzania. The males of this form have an intense lemon-yellow body coloration with a black-edged anal fin and whitish-blue highlights in the unpaired fins. They are found in shallow near-shore habitat where large rocks exist. Remarkably, an almost identically coloured sister species is found at Chitende Island, Malawi (Konings, 1989), nearly 100 km to the south, on the west coast of Lake Malawi! In the same area south of Matema, Tanzania, another species *P. sp.* "Zebra Goldbreast" is found over medium-sized rock habitats at depths of 10 metres. Males of the Zebra Goldbreast are light blue with vertical black bars, and light

blue unpaired fins dappled with yellow. Most notable is their yellow-orange throat and pelvic areas. Again we find a similar sister population of *P. sp.* "Zebra Goldbreast" at Hora Mhango, Malawi (Konings, 1989), over 130 km to the south, and again, across the lake on the west coast. Likewise, another Zebra-type species exists in identical sister populations on both the Tanzanian and Malawian coasts. The *P. sp.* "Zebra Pearly" is found at Cape Kaiser, Tanzania on the east coast; an identical morph is found at Ruarwe, Malawi, (Grant, pers. comm.) on the west coast of Lake Malawi. On the Malawian west coast the Pearly Zebra is found from Mdoka to Mara Rocks. The distance between the two sister populations of "Pearly" Zebras is 100 km on a skewed northeast to southwest axis. It is interesting to note that all three pairs of sister species mentioned above are not found directly across Lake Malawi from each other, but rather at geographical locations over twice the distance compared to the lake's width. A geographical variant of *Labeotropheus trewavasae* found at Cape Kaiser, Tanzania, is separated by almost 100 km from its sister populations on the Malawi side at Mpanga Rocks, Hora Mhango, and Nkhata Bay. This white top or blue morph of *L. trewavasae* is found on the eastern side in shallow, near-shore areas where large rocks exist. Again, these sister morphs are found not directly across the lake but along a skewed northeast to southwest axis. Interestingly, the "Red Stripe" isolant of the blue *L. trewavasae* is found south of Cape Kaiser in Tanzania and north of Nkhata Bay in Malawi. The two "Red Stripe Trewasasae" populations are separated by well over 100 km on a northeast-southwest axis. Some of the geographically separated sister populations of Lake Malawi are very similar, but not identically coloured. A yellowish *Cynotilapia* morph is found on both sides of Lake Malawi in the northern end: *Cynotilapia* sp. "Purple/Yellow" from Cape Kaiser, Tanzania, looks very much like the *Cynotilapia* sp. "Lion" found at Lion's Cove, Malawi (over 120 km south-southwest). Males of both species exhibit a golden yellow body coloration with light blue highlights and similarly coloured caudal fins. The black submarginal stripe in the dorsal fin and the lack of black body bars on the *C. sp.* "Purple/Yellow" are

notably different. However, both cichlids do occupy the same habitat at their respective locations—the sand-rock intermediate zone at a depth
of 10 metres. Do these similar morphs share a
common ancestry, or are they examples of convergent evolution?

The Malawian coast and the Tanzanian coast
converge in the extreme north where four major
rivers (Songwe and Kiwira the largest) enter the
lake (Johansen, pers. comm.). In addition, no
continuous rocky
outcrops connect
the opposing
shorelines, mak-
ing it difficult to
envision the rise
of identical spe-
cies on separate
and opposite
shores. While it is

P. sp. "Tropheops Chitande Yellow"
at Chitande Island, Malawi.

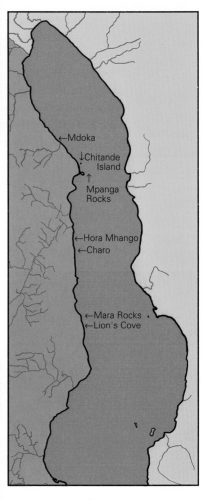

▲*Labeotropheus*
trewavasae at
Mpanga Rocks.

◀ *P.* sp. "Zebra
Goldbreast" at
Charo.

▼*P.* sp. "Zebra
Pearly" at Mpanga
Rocks.

true that large
vegetation mats
can frequently be
seen floating in
these waters,
w a n d e r i n g
mbuna "hitching a
ride" under these
mats is an un-
likely explanation
for the occurrence
of sister populations. Then how do these several
pairs of separated but similar populations of
cichlids find themselves on opposite sides of the
ninth biggest lake in the world? Konings (1992)
describes a similar phenomenom in the southern
part of Lake Tanganika where several near identical but separated cichlid fishes are found on
completely opposite shores. Konings attributes
his observations to a process of division of a
unified population which existed when the water
level in the lake was much lower than it is today.

Cynotilapia sp. "Lion" at Lion's Cove. Photos Ad Konings.

P. sp. "Macrophthalmus Bright Yellow" at Ikombe, Tanzania.

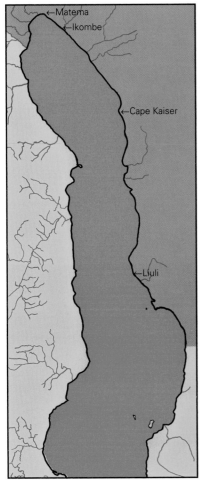

▲*Labeotropheus trewavasae* at Cape Kaiser.

▶ *P. sp.* "Zebra Goldbreast" at Ikombe.

▼*P. sp.* "Zebra Pearly" at Cape Kaiser.

Cynotilapia. sp. "Purple/Yellow" at Cape Kaiser. Photos Laif DeMason.

Over time, and with increasing water levels, the fishes were forced up newly submerged slopes (vertical migration) thus dividing the mother population into two sub-populations on geographically opposite shores. Could the same process have occurred in the northern end of Lake Malawi? Undoubtedly the same natural processes have occurred in each lake. Both lakes are now deeper and larger than in the distant past. While there are indeed many similarities, some of the biological results of this geographical separation process differ slightly, thus raising further questions regarding natural speciation processes. Some of the examples in Konings' (1992) article about Tanganyika cichlids occur nearly opposite from each other on an east-west axis, (for example, *Ophthalmotilapia ventralis* from M'toto, Zaïre and from Cape Mpimbwe, Tanzania). However, most of the Malawian sister populations occur not on a simple east-west axis across the lake, but diagonally at greater distances. All of the populations of Tanzanian shore cichlids noted here occur not only geographically opposite, but northward by 100 km in relation to their Malawian shore sister populations, As both Lake Malawi and Lake Tanganyika lie in geological rifts, perhaps tectonic shifts in the earth's crust could explain such differences in sister population locations.

However, a more plausible biological and geological solution is evident. Certainly one must keep in mind some relevant facts: as lake levels increase —a filling process— the lake not only becomes deeper, but wider and longer as well! Over geological time, there have been climatic changes during which prolonged wet periods reflect times of relatively rapid increases in lake levels and sizes, while during prolonged dry periods these processes are reversed. Therefore changes in size of Lake Malawi over the last 50,000 years have not been continuous. Take, for example, an ancient lake level 25,000 years ago in the extreme north of then Lake Malawi. At that end, there existed an hypothetical rock-dwelling mbuna species X. As lake levels increased rapidly, new and unsuitable habitat (river deltas) developed or increased at the extreme north, forcing an ecologically based division in the original population of species X. As lake levels continued to rise and widen, and because of a lack of suitable habitats in the northern, newly submerged areas, species X now had to migrate vertically to suitable submerged habitat, all the time becoming geographically further away from its sister population on the opposite shore. This process could continue with further lake increases of both size and levels (see illustration). Most of the Tanzanian shore cichlids mentioned earlier occur near the Livingstone Mountain area, which includes some of the highest mountains in East Africa. Furthermore most of the Malawian shore sister populations occur near the Viphya Mountains. Moreover Lake Malawi is deepest near these mountain areas in the north. One can surmise, with the present day topography of the extreme north (Kipengere Range) in mind, that rivers have been flowing into Lake Malawi creating unsuitable habitat for mbuna there for some time. While newly submerged habitat would be available for migrating mbuna along the Livingstone Mountains (east), the new areas to the northwest in the lake were no doubt sandy from river deposits and thus unsuitable for rock-dwelling cichlids. Perhaps this also may explain why these identical sister mbuna populations of Lake Malawi occur diagonally skewed. In other words, the sandy areas of the lake "bulged" to the north west as levels increased and thus located sister mbuna populations as we find them today. Certainly both Lake Malawi and Lake Tanganyika hold many clues to the exact nature of speciation and evolution. Further study of and insight into cichlid populations in Lake Malawi will yield better understanding of these biological phenomena.

Acknowledgements

I would like to thank E. S. Johansen, and the staff of Lake Nyasa African Fisheries (LANYAFI) for their assistance and co-operation in all the expeditions we made along the Tanzanian coast of Lake Nyasa.

References

DEMASON, L. (1992) New mbuna from the. Tanzanian coast of Lake Malawi. *Cichlid News* 1 (1), p: 17-19, 24-25.
KONINGS, A. (1989) *Malawi cichlids in their natural habitat.* Verduijn Cichlids & Lake Fish Movies. Netherlands.
KONINGS, A. (1992) Clues to a step-wise speciation. pp: 6-9; in: A. Konings (Ed.) *The Cichlids Yearbook Volume 2,* Cichlid Press, St. Leon-Rot, Germany.

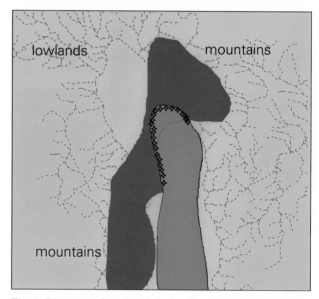

Fig. 1: Diagram of ancient lake levels showing surrounding terrain and suitable mbuna habitat (unified population) (❖❖).

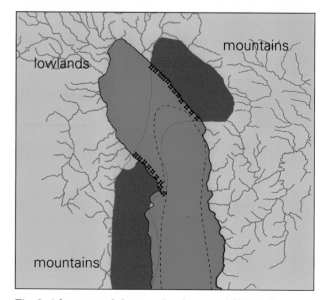

Fig. 2: After several thousands of years of filling, the ancient population now occurs as two separate sister populations.

Pseudotropheus sp. "Daktari"

Annette Bentler

Pseudotropheus sp. "Daktari" is collected on a submerged reef, named "Hai Reef", in the southern part of Tanzania close to its border with Mozambique. The substrate of the biotope consists of sand mixed with numerous pebbles and small rocks. Larger rocks lie scattered on the bottom which makes this biotope more of an intermediate type rather than a pure rocky one. At this relatively small and isolated reef *Ps.* sp. "Daktari" is fairly common. Most individuals are found at

also found in females, which have a beige-yellow coloration. In a later import of this species a yellow coloured mouthbrooding female was found among many normally coloured ones.

In its natural habitat *Ps.* sp. "Daktari" attains a length of about 10 cm (for males —females rarely grow larger than about 8 cm). Probably in order to have a better view of the territory, dominant Daktari males hover about one metre above the substrate. Females, however, are much more

Pseudotropheus sp. "Daktari" was first imported in April 1992 by Mal-Ta-Vi in Germany.

a depth of between 4 to 5 metres. In the same habitat I found *Cynotilapia afra*, several species of the *Ps. zebra* complex, *Melanochromis labrosus*, and several *Labidochromis* species. Besides these mbuna I also observed several different *Aulonocara* species and some large predatory cichlids.

The body shape of *Ps.* sp. "Daktari" is elongate, similar to that of *Ps. elongatus*. The outer teeth are bicuspid; the inner rows consist of tricuspid teeth. Dominant males have a bright orange-yellow coloration. Each scale has a shiny blue spot, resembling those in *Ps. lombardoi*, which enhances the brilliance of the yellow colour. A conspicuous feature in the colour pattern of *Ps.* sp. "Daktari" is the black upper and lower edges of the tail, a feature which is commonly found in species of the *Ps. elongatus* complex. These markings are

seclusive and remain close to the rocks. Spawning is preceded by the male leading the female to his nest. Spawning takes place on a rock in the territory and proceeds in the manner well-known for mbuna. The incubation period is about 20 to 22 days after which the female releases the fry. The spawns that I have observed contained only small numbers of fry which were abandoned immediately after release.

In colour, behaviour, and habitat preference *Ps.* sp. "Daktari" resembles a race of *Pseudotropheus* sp. "Lime" which is found at Membe Point, Likoma Island. Systematically we could group this mbuna, because of its elongated body and the black edges in the tail, with the species in the *Ps. elongatus* complex. It seems that *Ps.* sp. "Daktari" is an undescribed mbuna species.

Pseudotropheus sp. "Elongatus Chewere"

Ad Konings

Pseudotropheus sp. "Elongatus Chewere" has already gained a firm place among the popular cichlids from Lake Malawi.

ln May 1989, Walter Dieckhoff, Saulos Mwale and I found a small reef off the coast of Chewere, a small fishing village in the northern part of the lake. We were struck by a rather dense population of a hitherto unknown species of the *Pseudotropheus elongatus* complex, later named *P.* sp. "Elongatus Chewere". It was the only member of this complex at this site. Females and non-territorial males gathered in large foraging schools in midwater about one to four metres above the substrate. Most of the individuals were found at the transition zone between the rocks and the sand at a depth of about 16 metres. Territorial males defended their nests, some of them only about 50 cm apart, against all intruders. Most nests were dug beneath a rock or were on the sand between two adjacent rocks.

Perhaps because of a frequently occurring plankton-bloom or to a relative lack of competing species, a large population of an *elongatus*-type of Mbuna is able to inhabit this small reef. Members of the *P. elongatus* complex are known to feed on plankton at several other locations around the lake, but seldom forage in large schools. *P.* sp. "Elongatus Chewere" looks rather different from the yellow-barred *P.* sp. "Elongatus Chailosi" from Chitande Island, geographically speaking the closest population of an *elongatus*-type Mbuna. These two species live about 10 km apart and seem to have the same habitat preference. We could not find similar habitats between these two locations which could possibly harbour intermediate forms of the two species. These two species are apparently so restricted to their particular location that 10 km of barren sand is sufficient to maintain such a profound difference between them. Yet other species, noted for their preference for pure rocky habitats, e.g. species of the *P. tropheops* complex, are found in indistinguishable populations separated by much more than 10 km of sand. Probably the success of a species in the local community plays an important role as well.

The Yellow Black Line

Part 1: The current generic placement of *Haplochromis melanonotus* Regan by Ad Konings
Part 2: Aquarium observations by Peter Baasch

Mylochromis melanonotus is a regularly seen predator of the sandy habitat. Photo taken at Eccles Reef, Malawi.

Part 1

Platygnathochromis melanonotus has been known among aquarists, under the trade name "Yellow Black Line", for quite some time. Observations in the lake revealed that in one group of *P. melanonotus* —a breeding group at Eccles Reef was seen in December 1989— individuals with differences in the structure of the lower jaw were present. It has also been noted by aquarists that some individuals, usually large males, of the Yellow Black Line have a very flat lower jaw while the jaw in other members of the group shows a more normal aspect. Old specimens which have been raised in the aquarium show a flat lower jaw although not to the same degree as is seen in wild caught individuals.

The individuals with a flattening of the lower jaw were assigned to *Haplochromis melanonotus* Regan, and because of the very peculiar shape of this jaw Eccles & Trewavas (1989) erected a new genus to accommodate this species: *Platygnathochromis*. The individuals with a normally shaped lower jaw were described as *Haplochromis semipalatus*

Trewavas (1935), and this species was later included in *Maravichromis* (Eccles & Trewavas, 1989). *Maravichromis* has subsequently been shown to be a junior synonym of *Mylochromis* Regan, 1920 (Derijst & Snoeks, 1992). The only difference between the two species is the structure of the lower jaw: *M. semipalatus* has the same yellow coloration and the same morphological characteristics as are described for *P. melanonotus*. The fish which I have wrongly assigned (Konings, 1989: 237; 1990: 226) to *M. semipalatus* is probably an undescribed species.

On the basis of the observation that within one breeding community individuals with differences in the lower jaw structure were found, I regard *M. semipalatus* as a junior synonym of *Platygnathochromis melanonotus* (Regan).

The flattening of the lower jaw could be a phenotypic adaptation to the type of habitat in which the fish lives or to the type of food that it eats. Swollen lips, found in some other species, are generally recognised as phenotypic adaptations to feeding from rocky substrates. The same species usually do not develop such swollen lips in captivity and such lips are likewise not found in individuals caught over sandy substrates. The extreme flattening of the lower jaw in the Yellow Black Line may be an adaptation to the way this species feeds. I have observed several times that it scoops its prey, probably small fishes or similarly sized invertebrates, from the sand. The Yellow Black Line, which has a lower pharyngeal jaw set with fine teeth, may not have developed a technique for sifting the sand like many other species do—sand-filtering species normally have thickened teeth on the lower pharyngeal jaw. Moreover, the behaviour of this cichlid in its natural habitat points to that of a piscivore rather than to a sand-sifting predator. A flat lower jaw neatly separates the stalked prey from the substrate and thus avoids the intake of sand. However, there could be individuals which prefer to stalk their prey in the more rocky or perhaps muddy biotopes. These would, if we accept the hypothesis given above, not need to develop a flat lower jaw. Therefore I am of the opinion that the Yellow Black Line can be accomodated in the genus *Mylochromis* and that there is no need to define a separate genus for it. With regard to the feeding behaviour of *M. melanonotus*, it is interesting to note that on a number of occasions this species has been observed to be drawn to large black catfishes (or to me, dressed in a black diving suit). Once I observed that several individuals attacked a breeding pair of the catfish *Bagrus meridionalis* (Kampango) and tried to snatch the fry out of the nest.

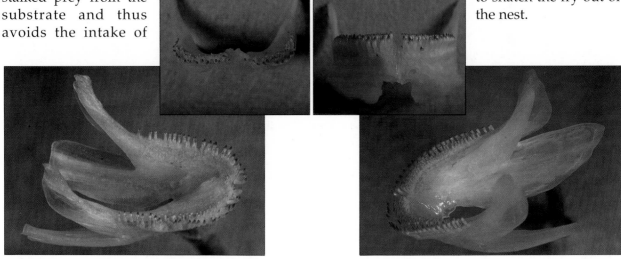

A dorso-lateral and a frontal view of the lower jaw of two individuals *M. melanonotus* from Eccles Reef. Right column: male, total length 158 mm. Left column: female, total length 178 mm. Photos Gertrud Dudin.

Part 2

Observations have shown that the Yellow Black Line is distributed throughout the lake and is found in several different habitats. Most individuals, however, were observed over sand where they forage on their own. The Yellow Black Line is characterised by a yellow colour in the fins and on the body, especially the anterior part. In non-breeding individuals a deep black diagonal line is visible, running from the dorsal part of the head, just in front of the dorsal fin, to the caudal peduncle. In breeding males the diagonal band disappears while vertical barring becomes visible. The specific name, *melanonotus*, which means "black back", alludes to this diagonal band because it runs over the upper part of the body.

Not much is known about the natural diet of the Yellow Black Line. However, in captivity it appears to be an easily satisfied cichlid which eats the common fare. I have noticed that the leaves of *Anubias* in tanks in which *M. melanonotus* was kept showed marks as if pieces had been chopped off. It is unclear whether this is done by the Yellow Black Line and if so, whether they do this habitually.

The general impression of the Yellow Black Line in the aquarium is that of a sand-dwelling cichlid. They are quite active and relatively peaceful towards other inhabitants of the tank. Breeding males defend a territory and build a shallow sand nest. Males energetically court females and try to lead them to their nest. After the female has been led to the centre of the nest, where the male attracts the female's attention by vibrating his anal fin, spawning may begin. As soon as the eggs are deposited they are picked up by the female. The male again displays his anal fin and discharges his seminal fluid. The female snaps at the male's vent, inhales the milt, and thus fertilises the eggs just laid. Mouthbrooding females are difficult to recognise because the buccal pouch is only slightly distended. Spawns normally result in about 60 fry which are relatively large when released. Juveniles grow rapidly and start to colour when they have a length of about 10 cm. The maximum size of *M. melanonotus* is around 25 cm for males and 20 cm for females.

The eggs are collected by the female. Photo Peter Baasch.

A breeding male lacks the diagonal band on the upper part of the body. Photo Peter Baasch.

References

DERIJST, E & SNOEKS, J. (1992) *Maravichromis* Eccles and Trewavas, 1989, a junior synonym of *Mylochromis* Regan, 1920 (Teleostei, Cichlidae). *Cybium* 16 (2): p 173.

ECCLES, D.H. & TREWAVAS. E. (1989) *Malawian cichlid fishes. The classification of some haplochromine genera.* Lake Fish Movies, Herten, Germany.

KONINGS, A. (1989) *Malawi cichlids in their natural habitat.* Verduijn Cichlids, Zevenhuizen, Netherlands.

After the eggs have been collected the female is attracted to the male's vent. Photo Peter Baasch.

Champsochromis caeruleus Boulenger, 1908

Edwin Reitz

A breeding male *Champsochromis caeruleus*. Photos Edwin Reitz.

To date two species have been assigned to the genus *Champsochromis*, *Ch. caeruleus* and *Ch. spilorhynchus* (Regan 1922). The first of these has a slender, in cross-section almost round, body, and is hence appropriately designated "Trout Cichlid", while *Ch. spilorhynchus* is somewhat more compressed and deep-bodied in appearance. Both are strong and rapid swimmers, and both have a deeply cleft mouth.

They are thus best suited to a predatory way of life in open water, much like the genera *Rhamphochromis* and *Diplotaxodon*. Just like these *Ch. caeruleus* is a true piscivore, which is found throughout Lake Malawi, down to depths of 55 metres (Eccles & Trewavas, 1989). Specimens over 15 cm in length remain by preference in open water, where their main prey is the lake sardine "Usipa" (*Engraulicypris sardella*). Adult specimens are solitary with a very high "flight distance": Horst Walter Dieckhoff reports that it is not possible to approach closer than 10 metres when diving before they flee.

Although *Champsochromis* are old acquaintances, for a long time little information was available about these attractive predators. Later on a few semi-adults were caught and exported, and since then breeding has been achieved several times. In

one respect their maintenance makes special demands on their owner: the aquarium cannot be too large. It should be at least 2 metres long and have a capacity of 500 litres or more. There are no positive data on the eventual size of the species, but it can be assumed that males attain more than 30 cm.

In captivity *Ch. caeruleus* do not abandon their natural way of life. They swim around a lot and are very aggressive towards each other. Feeding is no problem, as they eat practically anything. Frequent visits to the freezer are important, however, as they prefer food such as krill, shrimp, or *Mysis*. In addition feeder fishes up to about 6 cm in length are beneficial to their well-being. Males colour up at about 20 cm, giving a foretaste of the finery they display when breeding.

There is advance indication of imminent spawning some days before the event itself. The ripe female is courted vigorously by the male. The assertion that male and female form a pair is quite correct. In Lake Malawi these fishes are sometimes found in pairs. What at first sight appears surprising does actually make sense: males have no territory and no fixed spawning site. The female enters into a loose association with a male and is then led to a suitable spawning site. In the aquarium the spawning site is an open sandy surface, which is not modified and is given only a cursory cleaning by means of circling movements by the male. During spawning the pair position themselves almost parallel to each other, with the head of the male directed somewhat in the direction of the female's tail. The male releases his milt and uses his anal fin to fan it over the eggs while the female is laying them. The fishes are now at right angles to each other and momentarily adopt a T-position. This procedure is repeated several times, sometimes without the female laying any eggs.

A young female will lay some 50 to 80 eggs (2.5 mm diameter), while older specimens may produce more than 200. When spawning is completed the *caeruleus* male returns to his true character. The female is chased and may even be harmed if the aquarium is too small. In such cases the brood is usually lost. The space requirements of *Champsochromis caeruleus* mean that it is not suitable for everyone to keep. But if provided with a large aquarium this species can be kept with other Lake Malawi cichlids, eg *Aristochromis*, *Buccochromis*, *Dimidiochromis*, *Rhamphochromis*, *Stigmatochromis*, and *Tyrannochromis*.

Reference

ECCLES, D.H. & TREWAVAS. E. (1989) *Malawian cichlid fishes. The classification of some haplochromine genera.* Lake Fish Movies, Herten, Germany.

While the female expels some eggs the male waits in an almost parallel position besides her.

The female collects the eggs which appear to be fertilised afterwards inside her mouth.

Copadichromis chrysonotus (Boulenger, 1908)

Peter Baasch

Copadichromis chrysonotus, a breeding male with a size of about 7 cm!

Copadichromis chrysonotus is a plankton-feeding cichlid from Lake Malawi and has been imported recently. Cichlids with this name have been around in the hobby for much longer. Several species have been known to aquarists under the name of *Haplochromis chrysonotus*. Although these species show the characteristic three spots on the flank they should be referred to a different name. In particular the blue coloured cichlids from the islands of Mbenji and Maleri were, and still are, referred to as *Copadichromis chrysonotus*. In 1990 Konings described this species as *C. azureus*. Females and non-breeding males of several utaka with the three-spot pattern can be confused with *C. chrysonotus*. In aquaristic literature *C. chrysonotus* has also been confused with *C. jacksoni*. The latter is a much larger cichlid and has a more elongated body. *C. jacksoni* has only two spots on the flank which should be a simple character for distinguishing the two species. In practice this does not seem to work well; freshly caught individuals of *C. chrysonotus* often do not show the middle spot. Even in a tank the middle spot is not always distinct. Moreover, *C. jacksoni* and *C. chrysonotus* are usually found together.

The true *C. chrysonotus* is distributed throughout the lake and does not show geographical variation. With their brilliant coloration —without doubt *C. chrysonotus* is one of the most attractive cichlids from the lake— breeding males can even be seen from the boat.

Observations in the lake reveal that this species lives in somewhat calmer regions in midwater, usually above a rocky substrate. Male and female feed on zoo-plankton and gather in (sometimes large) schools. *C. chrysonotus* is the only (known) utaka which spawns in midwater. Territorial males defend a three-dimensional "nest", the boundaries of which are invisible. Neighbouring males defend a similar nest and stay at a fairly constant distance from each other.

Despite the fact that this species has a fantastic coloration and has been found at many different locations, it has never been exported commercially (Stuart Grant, pers. comm.). Two reasons may explain this situation. Firstly *C. chrysonotus* lives in midwater and is therefore very difficult to catch. The second, more important, reason is its fragility. My own experience with this species, freshly caught from the lake, was rather frustrat-

Copadichromis chrysonotus, a female.

ing. Despite continuous water changes females died within 30 minutes of collection; all males collected were dead the following day. Seen in this light it may be understandable that this species has not yet been exported commercially.

I received my *C. chrysonotus* as juveniles of about 2 cm, and although juveniles are much easier to transport and to maintain I had difficulties in keeping them alive for the first few weeks. After they have settled in the aquarium they are as easy to keep as most other utaka from Lake Malawi. The typical breeding technique of *C. chrysonotus* can also be observed in the aquarium. Males defend the highest possible point in the tank and court females relentlessly. When a ripe female follows a leading male spawning usually occurs a few centimetres above the male's "rock" (the true midwater spawning procedure was not observed in my aquaria). Male and female circle in very tight rounds, moving away from the "rock" in the process. During circling milt and eggs are released. The eggs sink to the bottom and are quickly picked up by the female immediately after she has discharged them. Unfortunately our tanks are not deep enough to allow them to display their midwater spawning procedure; in the lake their spawning site is several metres above the rocks.

The spawns are relatively small, usually numbering about 10 to 20 eggs. The eggs, however, are rather big (about 4 mm) and so are the fry when they are released. Juvenile *C. chrysonotus* grow fast and start to breed at a size of about 6 cm and at an age of about 6 months! Numerically spawns from such small females are even smaller but the eggs are the same large size as those from fully

mature females. At a length of about 6 cm dominant males get their fantastic colours (chrysos = golden; notus = back). The dorsal fin, forehead, and the upper part of the body become beige-yellow. The yellow colour in displaying males changes to a brilliant white-blue which extends into the upper part of the tail. The intraspecific aggression of this cichlid —maximum size of males is about 15 cm; females are much smaller— is limited to display, which makes it possible to keep more than one male together. The aquarium should be as deep as possible (breeding technique!) and preferably longer than one metre. After acclimatisation *C. chrysonotus* appears to be a rather robust cichlid which can be housed with many other Malawians. Tank-raised juveniles are as strong as those of most other utaka. Its unique spawning behaviour and fantastic coloration make *C. chrysonotus* a welcome addition to our aquaria.

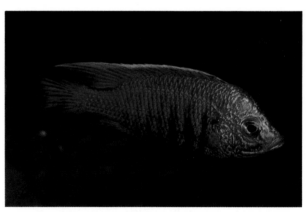
Copadichromis azureus at Nkhomo Reef.

C. jacksoni at Likoma Island. Photo Peter Frank

VICTORIAN CICHLIDS

Part 2: The oral shelling/crushing molluscivores

Ole Seehausen

In this article a number of haplochromines will be discussed that form a subgroup within the trophic group of the molluscivores (Witte & van Oijen, 1990). Once again I want to stress that trophic groups are ecological units free of direct phylogenetic implications. Some members of a trophic group might be closely related but others may have developed similar ecological and morphological characters independently of each other by convergent evolution. The article is based on my field work in 1989, '91 and '92 as well as on former publications.

What are oral shellers/crushers?

A rather large number of haplochromine cichlids in Lake Victoria exploit(ed) molluscs (snails and bivalves) as their major food source. Witte & van Oijen, 1990 described two subtrophic groups: "oral shellers/crushers" and "pharyngeal crushers" on the basis of different feeding techniques. Species of the latter group crush the shells between the pharyngeal bones ("pharyngeal mill"). The alternative way to wrench the soft body from the shell is employed by "oral shellers" (op.cit.). Laboratory work of Slootweg (1987) has shown that these groups are not strictly separated but species of both are able to crush mollusc shells intrapharyngeally, albeit with different efficiency. He demonstrated that oral shellers, when offered snails with low crush resistance (*Biomphalaria glabrata*), prefer to crush their prey intrapharyngeally if the shell size allows. I examined stomach/intestine contents of individuals of seven species of oral shellers and my data confirm Slootweg's results. Even in the lake all examined species are crushing small prey items and in

several these items make out the bulk of food in the intestine. Based on these results I would rather like to describe the dichotomy in molluscivorous feeding behaviour as follows: All molluscivorous Victorian haplochromines can crush intrapharyngeally. By doing so they encounter limitations due to 1. crush resistance of prey items; 2. size of prey items. Interestingly each group of species has only solved one of these problems: 1. the pharyngeal crushers increased their crushing ability and are consequently able to prey upon species with shells of higher crush resistance (they will be discussed in a separate paper). 2. the oral shellers improved their ability to pull snails out of the shell and are thus able to feed upon larger prey that do not fit into the buccal cavity. The extent to which species of the two groups differ in feeding techniques thus depends largely on prey characteristics.

About the ecology of oral shellers

Besides pharyngeal crushing, two other feeding techniques have been actually observed. *Haplochromis sauvagei* approaches a snail carefully and observes it from a distance of not much more than mouth length, usually holding the head somewhat oblique and fixing the snail with one eye only. At a suitable moment it quickly snatches the foot of the snail, shakes it briefly and tears or bites it off while the rest of the flesh remains in the shell. This technique or a similar one is supposed to be the one used by most or all oral shellers for prey that cannot be crushed. Only for *Macropleurodus bicolor* (and *H. prodromus*) another technique has been described: Greenwood (1956) writes that the fish "approaches a snail from above, rapidly protruding the mouth in an attempt to snatch its prey from the substrate...there follows a series of short biting movements (with the oral jaws) which crush the shell and thus free the soft parts, which alone are ingested". Slootweg, however, found *M. bicolor* to perform only pharyngeal crushing and oral shelling. It would be interesting to analyse the constraints that are imposed by the different feeding techniques in combination with morphological characteristics. Each of the solutions to the problem must have advantages and disadvantages. Slootweg, 1987, applying an optimal foraging approach, found that the potential reward in biomass per second is of the same magnitude in shelling and crushing but the disadvantage of shelling is that the probability of successful shelling is very low. Further the predator has to wait for the prey to come out of its shell and the fish usually gets hold of only a part of the flesh while a large part remains "wasted" inside the shell (Slootweg, 1987: 5-50%; pers. obs.). However this disadvantage might be reduced by anatomical adaptations. I observed that snails often show two reactions to disturbance: withdrawal and a lateral tilting movement of the shell towards the source of disturbance. The more pointed and narrower the jaws of a fish are, the better it can reach the body of the prey in the angle between its shell and the substrate. It can also penetrate deeper into the shell and consequently obtain a larger piece of the flesh. The narrow mouth of forms of the *H. xenognathus* group together with long procumbent teeth serving as an extension of the jaws, may enable these fishes to use smaller snails. Apart from anatomical adaptations differences in adult size may result in prey size partitioning between species.

Oral shelling molluscivores are one of the most widely distributed trophic groups in the lake, having been known before the *Lates* upsurge from every region and from shallow habitats as well as from deep waters down to a depth of 32m (Witte & van Oijen, 1990). All of the known species apparently live a benthic life. This seems to be related to their diet since lacustrine molluscs are benthic organisms. Certain species appear to be rather restricted to hard substrate types and prey, apparently, mainly upon *Bellamya*. Among them are those forms that seem to be best adapted to oral shelling from a morphological point of view (including the two known oral crushers). To pull snails out of their shell, in the way described below, good visibility is needed and the snail must move on a hard substrate. Neither condition is met on a soft mud surface where snails may

Platytaeniodus degeni (Mwanza), threatened with extinction.

H. xenognathus (Mwanza), a blue male.

H. cf. *prodromus* (Mwanza), a species from deeper water. Obtained in 1989.

H. sp. "Red Tail Sheller", a small species from Kenya.

Macropleurodus bicolor (Mwanza), an oral crusher; threatened with extinction.

H. xenognathus (Mwanza), a male with a red flank and operculum; much resembling *Macropleurodus*. See photo page 51 for a blue male.

H. sauvagei from a Kenyan population.

H. plagiodon (Mwanza) a predominantly sand-dwelling species.

forage within the layer of debris. Among those (potential) oral shellers that appear to prey mainly upon sphaeriid bivalves, small pulmonates (Planorbidae) and ostracode crustaceans which are crushed rather than shelled, are many inhabitants of mixed sand/mud habitats (Witte, 1984b; pers. obs.). The morphologically specialised pharyngeal crushers often live over muddy substrates and use the mud inhabiting snail *Melanoides tuberculata* as major food source (cf. Hoogerhoud et al., 1983) the shells of which are more crush resistant than *Bellamya*, sphaeriide, pulmonate and ostracode shells (Hoogerhoud, 1986).

Important ecological factors that contribute to species segregation are thus depth and exposure to the wind.

I distinguish three macrohabitats on the basis of different faunas of oral shelling molluscivores: The exposed shallow waters, the sheltered shallow waters and the offshore deeper waters. The exposed shallow waters are, apart from rocks, pure sand beaches. In the sheltered areas, organic sedimentation takes place. As long as the substrate is not real mud but sand with a layer of organic debris, a species-rich fauna of oral shellers is present (see fig. 1). My data concerning the offshore fauna are sparse because not much is left there after the *Lates* upsurge. Greenwood (1957) as well as Witte & Witte-Maas (1978) had found more or less deep-water restricted oral shellers before the major faunistic changes. New sampling results of N. Bouton and me suggest that rock restricted oral shellers may exist as well.

Little is known about the reproduction. It appears that most species are spawning throughout the year but seasonal fluctuations in spawning activity exist (Katunzi, 1980). In aquaria *H. sauvagei* males create a spawning pit in the sand. The females release the juveniles for the first time after *ca.* three weeks and continue broodcare for an-

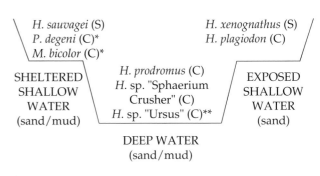

H. sauvagei (S)		H. xenognathus (S)
P. degeni (C)*		H. plagiodon (C)
M. bicolor (C)*		
SHELTERED SHALLOW WATER (sand/mud)	H. prodromus (C) H. sp. "Sphaerium Crusher" (C) H. sp. "Ursus" (C)**	EXPOSED SHALLOW WATER (sand)
	DEEP WATER (sand/mud)	

*before the *Lates* upsurge also in deeper water
**after Witte & Witte-Maas, 1978

Fig.1: Gross spatial distribution of some predominantly shelling (S) and predominantly crushing (C) oral shellers.

other week (pers. obs.). In the pre-*Lates* ecosystem the oral shelling/crushing molluscivores were probably the main mollusc consuming group of the sandy habitat (Witte & van Oijen, 1990). Anecdotal observations suggest that after the *Lates* upsurge the gastropodes have increased in many littoral areas (Witte *et al.*, 1992a). No data are available about haplochromines in the lake feeding on Schistosomiasis vector snails. Oral shellers were an important group for local fisheries.

Morphological characteristics of oral shellers

In most cases oral shellers can be recognised by a combination of dentition characteristics and a particular head shape. Oral teeth: outer row unicuspid or weakly bicuspid, slightly to strongly recurved and those in the lower jaw slightly to strongly procumbent (pointing forward). Inner teeth in 2 to 9 rows, in many species arranged in broad bands. Dorsal head profile usually steep, often convex. Lower jaw short and broad with a length/width ratio usually between 1 and 1.5 (Witte & Van Oijen, 1990). It is necessary to stress the fact that although a species that shows all these characteristics combined is likely to be an oral sheller, ecological data are necessary to confirm its trophic status. On the other hand a few oral shelling/crushing species do not share all the above-mentioned characteristics. Instead of unicuspid recurved teeth *Macropleurodus* has bicuspid oblique teeth with the major cusp pointing backwards and thus creating a curvature somewhat similar to that of recurved unicuspid teeth. Several forms retain a bicuspid dentition even when adult and have only 2(3) inner tooth rows, while procumbent implantation and recurvature are typical. In contrast *H. plagiodon* possesses bicuspid teeth with a flange, resembling those of algae grazers. These differences may not only reflect different adaptive levels and approaches but may also reflect different phylogeny.

The species

It cannot be stressed often enough that a picture and a brief discussion of a species cannot be used for reliable identification. The following rather aims at summarising some current knowledge to give an impression of diversity.
Macropleurodus bicolor (Boulenger, 1906) has been reported from all around the Lake (Greenwood, 1956). Before the Nile perch upsurge the species was particularly common in waters below 10 metres (*op.cit.*; Witte & Witte-Maas, 1978) over sandy substrates. The few individuals we collected in 1991/92 inhabited shallow water over mixed sandy-muddy bottoms and the sand-rock-reed interface. The species has apparently decreased considerably after the *Lates* upsurge. Among 1000 molluscivorous cichlids caught in 1991/92 eight were *M. bicolor* (0.8%). All were caught at only two localities. I would regard the species as threatened with extinction.
Hoplotilapia retrodens Hilgendorf, 1888 was widely distributed but apparently confined to rather shallow water over sand and was usually found near vegetation (Greenwood, 1956). It deviates from the typical oral sheller morphology by having a concave dorsal head profile and an extremely broad and almost rectangular, shovel shaped lower jaw, which, according to Greenwood (1956), is used as "a shovel when darting into or over the substrate". This species has disappeared from most of its former record localities and was not seen for several years. In 1991 K.M. Hamissi and I obtained two individuals at a place that appears to be a retreat area of some cichlids.
Platytaeniodus degeni Boulenger, 1906 is another species known from all parts of the lake. Before *Lates* it occurred in shallow as well as in intermediate waters (less than *ca.* 17m (Greenwood, 1956)) and fed mainly on detritus and pea-mussels (Katunzi, 1980). The species is extremely rare nowadays and in 1991 we caught a total of two males, both in shallow water over mixed sand-mud substrate. I consider it as threatened with extinction. *H. plagiodon* Regan & Trewavas, 1928 is known from Uganda (Entebbe) and Tanzania. In 91/92 Y. Fermon and I caught it as one of the most abundant species at exposed and less exposed sandy beaches in the Mwanza and Speke Gulf together with *H. xenognathus* and *H.* sp. "Bright Red Sheller". It was less common over sand-mud mixed bottoms.
The taxonomic status of *H. sauvagei* (Pfeffer, 1896) appears unclear. When Greenwood (1957) published his revision of this species, the holotype (apparently mislaid in Berlin Museum during the war) was not available. However, a photograph existed. This photograph (published in Greenwood, 1957) shows a fish which I doubt is conspecific with the fishes that were consequently (re)described as *H. sauvagei*. According to Seegers (pers. comm.) the holotype has been located recently. Pending further investigation I treat the form redescribed by Greenwood as *H. sauvagei*. His material came from all parts of the lake but his description of life colours fits only the northern populations. Males from Kenyan waters show a

copper-coloured to red sheen on the flanks which is virtually absent in specimens from Mwanza, but the major difference is the midlateral band which is continous in the former, but dissolved into longitudinal blotches in the latter. In the Mwanza area this species is found most abundantly over mixed sand-mud substrates in less exposed bays and at the rock-sand-reed interface. There it was still common in 1992.

H. sp. "Red Tail Sheller" is a small species resembling *H. sauvagei* in head and jaw shape. In contrast to the latter it has only 2(3) inner tooth rows and the outer teeth are bicuspid. As in *H. xenognathus* they are strongly procumbent in the lower jaw. It is known only from Kenya.

H. xenognathus Greenwood, 1957 is known from all parts of the lake and displays a wide range of variability within and between local populations. In some places males have a deep red sheen on flanks and operculum (strangely greatly resembling the coloration of *M. bicolor* and the Kenyan *H. sauvagei*), in others the red is absent, and both patterns can be found at the same spot. Apart from that, a completely red form is known (Witte, pers. comm.) that might be another species. *H. xenognathus* is still common at exposed sandy beaches, less common in sheltered bays with sand-mud bottoms. Over sand in the Mwanza region I found it sympatric with a similar species *H.* sp "Golden Xeno", which differs from *H. xenognathus* in coloration (the dark longitudinal bar is absent and males show a golden flush instead of blue), jaw morphology and dentition (fishes of respective size classes have more bicuspid teeth, the inner teeth are longer and arranged in only 2-3 rows). Examined intestines contained many sand grains sharply contrasting with those of *H. xenognathus* from the same catch. Its diet appears to be more insectivorous. The same holds for *H.* sp. "Bright Red Sheller" another sand-dwelling new species which shows broad bands of inner teeth. It is known only from one place in the Speke Gulf.

H. sp. "Sphaerium Crusher" might be a mud dweller. Its dentition comes closest to that of *H. xenognathus* but the outer teeth are less recurved and the inner teeth are arranged in 2-3 rows only. The intestine was full of shell fragments of sphaeriid bivalves and did not contain any sand grains. It was rare in 1989 and was not seen again afterwards. The species has to be compared with another bivalve-feeding mud-dwelling form that was collected by Witte & Witte-Maas (1978) under the name *H. xenognathus*-like (Witte, 1984b). Yet another form resembling *H. xenognathus* is

stored in BM(NH) as *H.* sp. "Deep-Water-Xenognathus". Witte & Witte-Maas (1978) collected a similar form at a market in Mwanza.

H. prodromus Trewavas, 1935, is an inhabitant of deeper, offshore, waters (Greenwood, 1957; Witte & Witte-Maas, 1978; pers. obs.). It has been reported from all parts of the lake including even the remote Godziba Island, but was apparently nowhere common. According to Greenwood it is an oral crusher with *Bellamya* as its main diet. The species may have suffered a serious decline.

H. granti Boulenger, 1906 is a large form with a thickened upper lip. It inhabits exposed sandy shores (Greenwood, 1957) in 0-4m depth (Witte & Witte-Maas, 1978; Witte, 1984b) but was nowhere common. I did not find this species in 91/92.

H. sp. "Ursus" is a new species collected by Witte & Witte-Maas (1978) in 12 to 18m depth over mud in the Mwanza Gulf entrance. The authors found remains of the gastropods *Bellamya* and *Melanoides* (mud dweller) in the stomach; the feeding technique is unknown but shell fragments suggest that it is at least partly crushing. The species was not caught anymore after 1983 (Witte *et al.*, 1992b). A new species, *H.* sp. "Striped Sheller", with a conspicuous head profile was caught by N. Bouton, R. Enoka, M. Khalifa, and myself in 1991 at a rocky island far from the shore in the Speke Gulf. It appears to be very rare or difficult to collect.

The oral shellers/crushers in the light of environmental changes

The degree to which haplochromines are affected by *Lates* depends on habitat, natural abundancy and adult size (Witte *et al.*, 1991). This apparently holds for the group discussed here as well. The species that were more or less restricted to deeper water (*H. prodromus*, *H.* sp. "Ursus", *H.* sp. "Xenognathus-like", and *H.* sp. "Sphaerium Crusher") apparently have greatly declined or may even be extinct. Likewise severely affected are *Macropleurodus* and *Platytaeniodus* which occurred in both shallow and deeper waters but probably had their gene pool centre in the latter. I regard both as threatened with extinction. By contrast the true shallow water species (often inhabitants of shallow sandy beaches) are still abundant.

Oral shellers/crushers in aquaria

To my knowledge seven or eight species exist in

H. sauvagei, a piebald male.

H. sp. "Bright Red Sheller", a new sand dwelling species.

H. sp. "Striped Sheller" from an offshore island. Photos Ole Seehausen.

aquaria. HEST (Haplochromis Ecology Survey Team) imported *H. xenognathus*, *H. sauvagei*, *Hoplotilapia retrodens*, *Macropleurodus bicolor*, *Platytaeniodus degeni*, all from Mwanza Gulf. All except *Hoplatilapia* have been included in the IUCN (Intern. Union for the Conservation of Natural Resources) breeding programme. *Hoplotilapia* is no longer present in HEST and IUCN stocks. I don't know whether a proper aquarium population still exists. In addition to the HEST populations, *H. xenognathus* (Kenya) and *M. bicolor* (Winam Gulf/Kenya) entered into the IUCN project. Bo Selbrink imported *H. plagiodon* into Sweden but it was unfortunately

distributed under the name *H. sauvagei* in Europe and *H.* "small spot" in the US. The identity of a fish that was imported by Selbrink as *H. prodromus* is unclear. It is unclear whether it is still present in Sweden. This is a pity because *H. prodromus* would perhaps be the most severely threatened of all the species which are kept in aquaria. Any information about any aquarium stocks would be highly welcome. Recently some littoral oral shellers were imported by ornamental fish traders from Kenya: *H. xenognathus*, *H.* sp. "Red Tail Sheller" and *H. sauvagei*, the latter from two populations. Both show a red flank in males but one has a continous longitudinal band while this is fragmented in the other one. Unfortunately they entered into the trade under a variety of incorrect names. From a conservation standpoint it is unsatisfactory that (except for *M. bicolor* and *P. degeni*) only littoral forms are kept in aquaria. Efforts should be made to rescue offshore species.

Acknowledgement

Many thanks to Frans Witte and Kees Barel for their recommendations on earlier versions of the manuscript.

Literature cited

HOOGERHOUD, R.J.C. (1986) Optimal prey processing in molluscivorous cichlids, Part I: The paradox of maximizing flesh- and minimizing shell-ingestion in *Astatoreochromis alluaudi* Pellegrin, 1903. Chapter 4 in: R.J.C. Hoogerhoud: Ecological morphology of some cichlid fishes. PhD Thesis, Leiden, Netherlands.

KATUNZI, E.F.B. (1980) *Food preferences of four haplochromine cichlids from Mwanza Gulf in Lake Victoria.* MSc thesis, 132pp, University of Dar es Salaam.

KATUNZI, E.F.B. (1983) Seasonal variation in the food of a molluscivorous cichlid *Haplochromis sauvagei* Pfeffer, 1896. *Neth. J. Zool.* 39 (3), pp: 337-341.

SLOOTWEG, R. (1987) Prey selection by molluscivorous cichlids foraging on a schistosomiasis vector snail, Biomphalaria glabrata. *Oecologia* 74: pp 193-202.

WITTE, F., GOLDSCHMIDT, T.,GOUDSWAARD, P.C., LIGTVOET, W., Van OIJEN, M. & WANINK, J.H. (1992a) Species extinction and concomitant ecological changes in Lake Victoria. *Neth. J. Zool.* 42(2-3), pp 214-232.

WITTE, F., GOLDSCHMIDT, T., WANINK, J., Van OIJEN, M, GOUDSWAARD, K., WITTE-MAAS, E., & BOUTON, N. (1992b) The destruction of an endemic species flock: quantitative data on the decline of the haplochromine cichlids of Lake Victoria. *Env. Biol. Fish.* 34: pp 1-28.

WITTE, F. & WITTE-MAAS, E.L.M. (1978) Reports from the Haplochromis Ecology Survey Team (HEST) 2: Annotated list of the haplochromine species: oral shellers/crushers. Leiden University. Distribution limited.

All other titles are given in Seehausen, O. (1992): Victorian cichlids. Part 1. In: A. Konings (ed.): *The Cichlids Yearbook. Vol. 2.* Cichlid Press. For reasons of space they cannot be repeated here.

Some new Victorian cichlids

Mark Smith

Haplochromis sp. "Parvidens Shovelmouth". Photos Mark Smith. Courtesy of Old World Exotic Fish Inc.

With all the attention focused on Lake Victoria's problems pertaining to cichlid extinction, it is now known that there are hundreds of new cichlid species that have been discovered since Greenwood's monumental work. Even though there has been a great amount of reduction in the number of various species, especially of the larger piscivorous types, nevertheless a surprising variety of cichlids continues to be found in the lake, even in such exposed groups as the piscivores. The three species which are briefly introduced here were all collected in Ugandan waters.

Haplochromis sp. "Parvidens Shovelmouth" attains a size of about 15 cm. A few individuals were collected and shipped with "Largemouth". Although the shape of its mouth indicates a benthic feeder, initial observations in the aquarium show it to be a piscivorous fish.

Only one specimen of *H.* cf. *dentex* has been imported. It had a size of approximately 16 cm. It appeared to be very reclusive in the aquarium where it stayed in the darkest portion near the back. Its mouth indicates it is a piscivore. Although its reclusive behaviour may point to an ambush hunter its streamlined body suggests a pursuit hunter.

H. sp. "Silver Stiletto" appears less aggressive and less nervous than most Victorian haplochromines currently in the hobby and even shows a slight tendency to form a loose school in captivity. At a size of about 10 cm the males seem to be mature and take on a more sooty coloration and less of a silvery colour.

The collecting of all these cichlids took place in water less than 10 metres deep. It has been suggested that because the deeper layers have become increasingly inhospitable to cichlid life, cichlids which are normally deeper dwelling gradually migrate into shallower water, which would perhaps explain why more species continue to be found.

Haplochromis sp. "Silver Stiletto".

Haplochromis cf. *dentex*.

WEST AFRICAN CICHLIDS

Hemichromis letourneauxi Sauvage, 1880

Jörg Freyhof

Anyone who wishes to catch cichlids will certainly not think of looking for them around the Mediterranean. But there is a "handful" of interesting species to be found there. Only a very small number are endemic to the Mediterranean region, but the type localities for a number of important African cichlids lie in this area. Quite simply, it used to be —and still is— easier of access than, for example, the central Congo, and for this reason was collected at an early date. Thus, for example, *Oreochromis niloticus* and *Sarotherodon galilaeus* were described as early as

1758 by Linnaeus himself, as *Sparus niloticus* and *Sparus galilaeus* respectively. *Tilapia zillii*, and finally *Hemichromis letourneauxi*, have their type localities in this region.

Hemichromis letourneauxi belongs to the Jewel Cichlid Group, which has been paid hardly any attention by systematists. By contrast those aquarists who are interested in colourful inmates for their aquaria have prized these cichlids for many decades and most cichlidophiles will have already made the aquaintance of this group on at least one occasion. The existence of several

The biotope of *Hemichromis letourneauxi* in Lake Maryut, Egypt. Photo Jörg Freyhof.

species of Jewel Cichlid was made manifest by Loiselle in his revision (1979) of the genus in which he split a single species (*Hemichromis bimaculatus*) into seven! He described 4 new species and two which had disappeared into synonymy were revived.

Hemichromis letourneauxi Sauvage, 1880 is one of these old, revived, species. According to Loiselle (1979; Ann. Mus. roy. afr. centr. sc. zool. 228: pp 1-124) this fish is distributed widely across Africa, and inhabits not only a number of Saharan oases, but also Lake Tchad, Lake Rudolf, the systems of the rivers Niger, Senegal, Gambia, Komoe, Bandama, Sassandra, and Volta, a few smaller rivers, and, finally, the Nile. Unfortunately Loiselle's data on the separation of this species from other Jewel Cichlids are so complex that I find myself unable to identify it on the basis of the revision. Luckily the type locality of this interesting species is by no means difficult to reach, but lies immediately behind the Mediterranean metropolis of Alexandria, in Lake Maryut. This lake is rela-

tively shallow and very slightly brackish. Huge reed beds modify the shape of the water's surface. The fish fauna is quite clearly dominated by cichlids. The vast majority of fishes caught by fishermen are tilapiines (*Tilapia zillii*, *Oreochromis niloticus*, *Oreochromis aureus*, and *Sarotherodon galilaeus*). Other fishes include, as well as the Jewel Cichlids we were seeking, the catfish *Clarias gariepinus*, the toothcarp *Gambusia holbrooki*, which is widespread all over Egypt, and the cichlids

The deep red colour of the female *H. letourneauxi*, collected in Lake Maryut, Egypt, make it to a very attractive cichlid.

A fry-guarding male *Hemichromis letourneauxi* originating from Lake Maryut, Egypt. Photos Jörg Freyhof.

Haplochromis cf. *flaviijosephi* and *Pseudocrenilabrus multicolor. Hemichromis letourneauxi* proved easy to catch with a hand net in the vegetation close to the shore. They were relatively common, but their numbers were clearly inferior to those of the ubiquitous *Haplochromis*. In March the Jewel Cichlids were without exception young fishes spawned during the previous year. Like all the cichlids in the lake *Hemichromis* probably has a distinct seasonality to its reproductive behav-

A female *H. letourneauxi* from Nigeria.

iour.
The fishes we collected survived transportation home in small plastic containers without difficulty, and grew on rapidly in the aquarium. Like all Jewel Cichlids they proved very resilient and soon the first pairs had formed. When the first

pair, in full coloration, led their fry around the aquarium it became evident that here was a species which could be clearly and easily distinguished from all the other *Hemichromis* known to me. Above all the red patterning in the female is characteristic of *Hemichromis letourneauxi*. It is the only Jewel Cichlid in which the red coloration in motivated females is always fainter from the centre of the body to the belly. In all other species (*bimaculatus, paynei, guttatus, lifalili, cristatus*) the red coloration is clearly most intense on the throat and breast. In addition this is a very small species, and not quite as boisterous as other fishes of this group. As it turns out, this fish has in fact been imported previously for the aquarium trade, but on that occasion the fishes came from Nigeria.

The identification of Jewel Cichlids is not easy, as in all species there may be considerable variation from population to population. In this case it is noticeable that the females of the two populations are almost identical in colour, while the males exhibit clear differences. This is a phenomenon which occurs in other *Hemichromis* species as well. It is not definite that the fishes from Nigeria mentioned here are truly conspecific with *H. letourneauxi*. We are acquainted with far too small a number of populations of the species to be positive. But they are certainly very closely related. Even though the distribution of the species corresponds to the data given by Loiselle, the uncertainty still exists. It is a fact that several species of Jewel Cichlids may occur sympatrically in a single area, so that, especially in West Africa, they cannot be identified on the basis of distribution maps. In the Niger Delta alone, for example, there are three different species of Jewel Cichlids (*guttatus, cristatus,* and *letourneauxi*). Thus the systematics of Jewel Cichlids are, and must remain, a closed book, whose pages will be opened only with difficulty.

A fry-guarding male *H. letourneauxi* from Nigeria.

Tylochromis leonensis Stiassny, 1989

Jörg Freyhof

The genus *Tylochromis* was erected in 1920 by C. Tate Regan during a critical review of African cichlids, in order to accommodate *Pelmatochromis jentinki* Steindachner 1894 and *Pelmatochromis polylepis* Boulenger 1900. In the same year Regan published a revision of the genus, a mere seven pages long, and assigned a further 6 species to *Tylochromis*, in the process splitting Boulenger's *Pelmatochromis lateralis* into 5 species. The genus thus contained 8 species, and it was not until 1954 that a further cichlid belonging to this lineage, *Tylochromis sudanensis,* was described by Daget. Thereafter *Tylochromis* remained unchanged until the publication in 1989 of a new revision by Dr. Melanie Stiassny, which demonstrated the extent to which a single group of fishes from West Africa can contain surprising new discoveries. Nine new species were described in this paper, doubling the existing number to a total of 18.

Included in these new species was the cichlid which is the subject of the current article. *T. leonensis* is a fish with a restricted distribution, whose main population is concentrated, as the name suggests, in Sierra Leone. It is also found in the adjacent western part of Liberia. This area belongs to the upper Guinea region. But it forms a relatively well defined zoogeographical entity with very ancient rain forests (which have practically disappeared) and a high element of endemism. This endemism is particularly evident in the cichlids. In the "Kolenta/Sierra Leone/Western Liberia region" there is a whole series of fishes which are found only in this area, for example *Sarotherodon caudomarginatus, Sarotherodon leonensis, Tilapia joka, Pelvicachromis roloffi,* and *Anomalochromis thomasi,* amongst others. The main body of *Tylochromis* species, however, is distributed across central Africa. West Africa, with 4 species, does not have very much to offer. The coastal rivers are inhabited by *T. jentinki* and *T. intermedius,* which may also occur syntopically with *T. leonensis.* The fourth *Tylochromis* (*T. sudanensis*) inhabits the Niger system and the rivers Cross and Wouri in central Africa, and is thus a typical savannah species.

We know practically nothing about the ecology of these animals. In Sierra Leone *Tylochromis* are typically cichlids of the large rivers. *Tylochromis leonensis* is a "Sand Fish", which inhabits large sandbanks and hardly ever penetrates into small

A freshly caught *Tylochromis leonensis*, Taia River near Taiama, Sierra Leone. Photos Jörg Freyhof.

Taia River near Taiama, Sierra Leone. Inset: *Tylochromis leonensis* showing the fright-pattern.

streams. We were regularly able to observe these fishes along sandy banks and in the middle of the river, where they were searching in the substrate for food, after the manner of *Geophagus*. Unfortunately we likewise know very little about the biology of these fishes. Only in the case of *T. jentinki* has the breeding behaviour been recorded —it is a maternal mouthbrooder (Amon-Kothias 1980). *Tylochromis leonenis* is also an ovophilous mouthbrooder, but we were unable to discover anything further in the natural habitat.

Unfortunately the few specimens we collected all turned out to be males, so there is still much new ground to be investigated. Perhaps the most interesting point is that these fishes evince a distinct seasonality in their breeding cycle. Thus in March, at the end of the dry season, there were numerous small juveniles and brooding individuals at the type locality, the Taia River in Sierra Leone. By contrast in October, shortly after the peak of the rainy season, there were no small juveniles to be found at all! In general we still know far too little about such phenomena in tropical rivers.

Tylochromis are completely unknown in the aquarium hobby, and hardly any cichlidophiles have ever actually seen one. They do not seem, however, to be particularly attractive as aquarium fishes. The majority of species grow to more than 20 cm in length and are rather dull in coloration. In captivity *Tylochromis* have been found to be both delicate and lively. With increasing size they also become rather quarrelsome, so that they can be kept together only in a relatively large tank. Nevertheless they are interesting fishes, which are attractive by virtue of their elegant and striking shape. *Tylochromis* are truly very unusual West Africans!

References

AMON-KOTHIAS, J.B. (1980) Reproduction et incubation buccale chez *Tylochromis jentinki jentinki* (Cichlidae). *Doc. Sci. cent. Rec. Oceanogr. Abidjan* XI (2): pp 1-38.

REGAN, C.T. (1920) A revision of the african genus *Tylochromis*. Ann. Mag. Nat. Hist. London (9)5: pp 163-169.

STIASSNY, M.L.J. (1989) A taxonomic revision of the african genus *Tylochromis* (Labroidei, Cichlidae); with notes on the realationships of the group. *Ann. Mus. roy. Afr. centr. sc.zool.* n258: pp 1-161.

Teleogramma brichardi Poll, 1959

Mary Bailey

Teleogramma is a genus of small, sexually dimorphic, rheophilic cichlids originating from the Zaïre River (formerly the Congo) and its affluents. At the time of writing four species are known to science, of which only one, *T. brichardi*, has been exported for the aquarium trade.

T. brichardi was first seen in Europe in the late 1960's and early 1970's, together with several other interesting West African species of the genera *Steatocranus*, *Pelvicachromis*, and *Nanochromis*. Of these, however, only *Steatocranus casuarius* became established in the hobby, and there are few records of any others being bred. *T. brichardi* was bred at least once, but failed to become estab-

Teleogramma brichardi. Photos Mary Bailey.

lished, and the aquarium population died out with the original wild stock. Subsequently political upheavals in Zaïre put an end to exports of aquarium fishes for some years, and it was not until the 1980's that *T. brichardi* was again available to aquarists.

The natural range of this species is limited to a comparatively short stretch of the lower Zaïre River near Kinsuka, to the south-east of Kinshasa; it is apparently replaced further downstream by two of its congeners, *T. gracilis* and *T depressum*. (The fourth species, *T. monogramma*, is restricted to the River Kasai, which drains into the Zaïre upstream of the *T. brichardi* locality.) Natural water conditions are reported as very soft, pH 7-7.5, temperature 28-29° C, and, obviously, a very

high oxygen content.

All four species inhabit areas of turbulent water where the river descends over rapids. All are more or less cylindrical in cross-section and extremely elongate, giving an almost snake-like appearance. All have the much reduced swim-bladder characteristic of rapids cichlids and seen also in *Gobiocichla*, *Steatocranus*, the fluviatile species of *Lamprologus*, and *Orthochromis* from Africa, and in the recently described analogous genus *Teleocichla* from Brazil. This modification is thought to enable them to remain resting on the bottom, unaffected by the rush of water overhead; buoyancy is not an advantageous characteristic for small fishes inhabiting fast-flowing waters which might easily sweep them away. It has to be said, however, that because of the difficulty of underwater studies in such conditions our knowledge of their natural lifestyle is, of necessity, largely surmise. We do not even know what foods are taken, though it is reasonable to assume a diet of aquatic invertebrates and crustaceans, probably with a degree of opportunism. *T. brichardi* relishes live foods such as *Daphnia* and chironomid larvae in captivity, and recently imported wild specimens show no hesitation in seizing and devouring whole earthworms.

The species exhibits marked sexual dimorphism, particularly at breeding time when the female is a medium grey with a large salmon-coloured area extending from the pectorals to the vent, covering the entire depth of the body and suffusing the lower part of the dorsal. The breeding male is, by contrast, uniform grey. Non-breeding females may show no red at all, or just a tinge on the belly, and the body becomes banded vertically in two shades of brownish-grey. Non-breeding males are very similar. Generally speaking males are larger (up to 12 cm SL) than females on an age for age basis, and the sexes can be easily told apart at all times by a characteristic marking in the tail. Both sexes have a white outer edging to the dorsal, and in males this continues onto the upper edge of the caudal. In females, however, the edging broadens to a large, forward pointing, triangle of white in the upper caudal. Interestingly these white markings appear red in preserved specimens (Roberts & Stewart, 1976), but in live fishes they are unequivocally a pure white. *Teleogramma brichardi* was merely a name to me until the publication of Linke & Staeck's volume on West African cichlids in 1981, after which I endured several years of unrequited longing before finally obtaining a pair in late 1985. I had read that there was liable to be considerable hostility between individuals (it is thought that this species, in common with some other rapids cichlid species, e.g. *Steatocranus tinanti*, lives solitarily except at spawning time), so they were given a fairly large aquarium. Within a few hours the male was chasing the female relentlessly, so I inserted a clear divider. A victimised fish usually takes refuge in an upper corner, and obviously this would be a far more serious situation for a fish with minimal buoyancy than for a "normal" cichlid, because of the need to expend energy swimming to remain *in situ*. It therefore seemed best to let them settle into individual territories before attempting a further encounter.

In the event this strategy proved highly successful, and when some weeks later the divider was moved slightly aside, to leave a 3-4 cm gap at the front of the tank, there was no hostility, even though each fish regularly ventured into the other's half of the tank. In fact there was little mutual interest shown at all, although a few weeks later I did see the pair indulging in a rather half-hearted display, resting alongside each other, head to head, on a flat stone. The only other interesting activity observed at this time was the method of digging employed by the female, which consisted of diving head-first into a small cave, "worming" her way forwards with gravel flying out behind her. I have never seen any other cichlid excavate a cave in this manner!

Spawning took place only much later, and quite unexpectedly. The female was found resting in her usual cave with a clutch of large (2.5 x 3.5 mm approx.) creamy-white eggs clearly visible on the ceiling. The spawning may, perhaps, have been triggered by a rise in temperature due to unseasonably sunny June weather which had raised fish-house ambient temperature to 28° C. The male was at some distance and showing no interest in the proceedings. All went well for three days, then I noticed that there appeared to be fewer eggs, and as I watched the female pulled one from the rock (with great difficulty, presumably the eggs need to be extremely adhesive to withstand the currents) and ate it; in consequence the rock was removed and the eggs hatched artificially -this was, after all, only the second known spawning in captivity.

The eggs were opaque and I feared they might be infertile, but the next day about 20 of the 30+ had hatched. It could then be seen that the infertile eggs were whiter than the creamy colour of the

Hatching eggs. The black band on the stone is 8 mm wide.

Female *T. brichardi* guarding her enormous eggs.

A female *T. brichardi* in breeding coloration. Photo Georg Zurlo.

others. The wrigglers remained firmly attached to the rock for a further six days; seven died during the wriggler stage, and another two after they became free-swimming, for reasons unknown. The fry were enormous (a *Tropheus* female would have been proud of them), measuring about 1.5 cm total length. Obviously large fry would be more likely to survive in turbulent conditions.

One or two further points are worth noting: firstly, there is little point in trying to simulate natural turbulence, as these fishes do not at all appreciate one's efforts. During experiments with an internal power filter with its outlet above the surface, the female perpetually sat under the filter itself, i.e. in the least turbulent spot available. When the filter was turned off she returned to her normal routine of patrolling her territory. The degree of aeration provided by moderate turn-over air-driven UG filtration has proven satisfactory with these fishes, as with several other species of rapids cichlids.

Secondly, despite the initial aggression of the male (and the species' reputation for intraspecific aggression), once territories had been established there was no further problem. I am not even sure that "territory" is the correct word to use, as neither fish showed any particular inclination to defend its own area. It has been suggested that territoriality in some rapids cichlids is linked to food supply rather than reproductive activity, so perhaps it can become superfluous in captivity where the ability to obtain sufficient food generally ceases to be a survival factor. Even when the

pair were moved to another smaller tank there was no resumption of hostilities, and a further small brood was raised without my intervention or (initial) knowledge.

The first batch of young were grown to sizes ranging from 5 cm (smallest female) to 8 cm (largest male) and lived together in amity with an average territory size only 10 cm or so in diameter, although there was a vertical component, with the smallest female based (literally) on the wire clip of the external thermostat!

Some years later another pair, already settled in captivity by a previous owner, presented no problems, although later still a newly imported pair proved considerably more troublesome, the female jumping a divider several times and eventually murdering the male. As neither of my two previous pairs had shown any such athletic tendencies I found this rather surprising, but have subsequently been told that it is by no means uncommon. Despite her single-minded persistence in bringing about the demise of the male, she has never shown the least inclination to attack other tankmates. This is in line with my experiences with other individuals, none of which, despite warnings to the contrary in the literature, has ever attempted to molest heterospecifics, even similar cichlids such as *Steatocranus tinanti*.

Importations of this species now seem to be more regular, so hopefully its future in the hobby will soon be assured by a significant degree of captive breeding, as it is by no means as difficult to maintain as originally indicated.

CENTRAL AMERICAN CICHLIDS

Herichthys tamasopoensis n. sp., a new cichlid from México (Pisces, Cichlidae)

Juan Miguel Artigas Azas

A fry-guarding pair of *Herichthys tamasopoensis* n. sp. photographed in a rocky pool in the Río Puente de Dios. Photo Juan Miguel Artigas Azas.

Abstract

A new cichlid fish of the genus *Herichthys* Baird & Girard, 1854 is described from the Río Pánuco system in northeastern México. The species is known among aquarists as Tamasopo *Herichthys*. By differences in morphology and behaviour in comparison to *Herichthys carpintis*, its closest relative, the Tamasopo *Herichthys* is distinguished as a species new to science.

Introduction

The genus *Herichthys* was erected by Baird and Girard in 1854. In the general characteristics given by these authors the structure of the teeth is of importance: "Teeth small, sub-conical, simple, exterior row most conspicuous". Meek (1914) suggested that the structure of the teeth is an ecophenotypic character and thus of minor importance in the definition of the genus. In his overview of the status of the name *Herichthys* Loiselle (1982) indicates that it is treated as a subdivision of *Cichlasoma sensu* Regan by most cichlid systematists. In 1983 Kullander restricted the genus *Cichlasoma* to 12 South American species and in 1986 he restricted the genus *Heros* to two species. The next available name for the Central American cichlids previously assigned to *Cichlasoma* is *Herichthys* (Burgess & Walls, 1992). The new species belongs to the same species group as *H. cyanoguttatus*, which is the type species of the genus, and is therefore assigned to *Herichthys*.

The closest relative of the new species, *Herichthys carpintis* (Jordan & Snyder, 1900), is found in the lower Río Pánuco basin and the Río Verde (it may have been introduced here (Taylor & Miller, 1983)) but is absent from the Río Gallinas. The new cichlid species described here is endemic to the Río Gallinas and its tributaries, which run mostly in the Tamasopo county of the Mexican state of San Luis Potosí. At an altitude of about 350 metres above sea level the Río Gallinas drains the Rascon valley. The new cichlid is geographically isolated from the rest of the cichlids in the Pánuco drainage by a waterfall 105 metres high at Tamul (99°13' W. Long., 21°12' N. Lat.). This geological barrier, where the Río Gallinas pours into the Río Tampaón, prevents upstream movement of fishes.

Measurements and counts were performed in accordance with Barel *et al.* (1977). The types were compared with freshly collected material of *H. carpintis*, five specimens of which originated from near the type locality: Laguna del Carpintero, Tampico. This lagoon was heavily polluted and subsequently has lost all of its fishes.

Herichthys tamasopoensis n. sp.

This species is known among aquarists as Tamasopo *Herichthys* (Artigas Azas, 1990).

Derivation of name

The name refers to the county Tamasopo where this cichlid occurs. This name has its origin in the indigenous (Huasteca Indian) word "Tam-Azote" meaning "place of waterfalls".

Diagnosis

A moderately deep bodied, laterally compressed member of the genus *Herichthys* which exhibits the characteristic feature of having the anterior teeth of the outer series in each jaw compressed and becoming truncated in the adult fish. It differs from its closest relative *H. carpintis* in having a

The oxygen-rich water in a rocky pool in the Río Puente de Dios supports a dense population of *Herichthys tamasopoensis* n. sp. Photo Juan Miguel Artigas Azas.

Herichthys carpintis caught in Laguna de la Altamira, Tampico. Photo Juan Miguel Artigas Azas.

Herichthys tamasopoensis n. sp. photographed in an aquarium. Photo Juan Miguel Artigas Azas.

shallower body (43.5-44.6% of standard length as opposed to 46.6-48.7% in *H. carpintis*), a shorter snout (37.5-40.7% of head length as opposed to 46.0-51.0%), a longer caudal peduncle (length 100% of its depth as opposed to 66.7-81.8% of its depth in *H. carpintis*), and in having a dorsal head profile which, even in fully grown specimens, does not form a concavity above the eye (on a straight line from the tip of the snout to the basis of the first dorsal spine). *H. tamasopoensis* also attains a smaller maximum total length of around 18 cm than does *H. carpintis* which may reach 22 cm in total length when fully grown.

In biological aspects *H. tamasopoensis* differs from *H. carpintis* in having an earlier reproductive cycle starting in mid December and ending around the end of May. In *H. carpintis* the breeding season, even if the environmental conditions are similar to those of *H. tamasopoensis*, ranges from the end of March through to the beginning of August.

Description (holotype in parentheses)

Body laterally compressed and deep; depth of body 43.5-44.6% (44.4%) of standard length (SL). Head length 30.6-32.6% (31.6%), snout length 37.5-40.7% (40.7%), depth of preorbital 29.6-34.6% (33.3%), and cheek depth 40.0-42.6% (41.1%) of SL. Dorsal head profile strongly curved, more curved from nape to first dorsal spine; its inclination in the paratypes ranges from 44° to 50°; the holotype, a breeding male, has a dorsal head profile inclination of 57°. Adult breeding males normally have a well developed nuchal hump. Eye length 27.4-30.8% (27.4%), eye depth 24.2-27.1% (24.4%), interorbital width 34.4-38.8% (37.4%), length of premaxillary pedicel 39.0-44.2% (40.7%) and length of lower jaw 35.3-42.2% (37.4%) of head length. The prominence of the premaxillary pedicels is slight to none. The pedicels have an inclination of 53° to 64° (64°).

Mouth isognathous; jaws with a rounded dental arcade. Teeth in the outer row compressed and truncate, 3 to 4 inner rows of small pointed teeth.

8 to 9 gill rakers on the lower part of the first arch, 1 to 3 of which are reduced, the others long and slender.

Scales ctenoid, 27 to 29 (28) in a longitudinal series; 17-19 (19) in the upper lateral line, 9-11 (9) in the lower. 4-6 (5) scales between the upper lateral line and dorsal fin and 5 scales between the pectoral and pelvic fins. 5 scales on the cheek.

Caudal fin sub-truncate; tip of anal fin extending beyond the basis of the caudal fin. Pectoral fin 24.2-26.9% (26.9%) and caudal fin 22.9-27.5% (27.5%) of SL. Dorsal fin XIV-XVII 9-11 (XVI 10), total 25 to 26 rays. Anal fin IV-V 8 (V 8). Caudal peduncle as deep as long.

Herichthys tamasopoensis n. sp., holotype (221577). Breeding male 85.5 mm SL.

Live coloration

Normal pattern: Ground colour light yellowish-green, greyish-green in some individuals. The yellow coloration fades when kept in an aquarium. Head and lips green, becoming darker dorsally. Gill covers and eyes light purple. Body covered with small, about one millimetre diameter, yellowish to light blue spots which are denser in and around the bases of the unpaired fins. Fins translucent with a salmon hue on the rostral part of the dorsal fin. Seven black blotches on the posterior half of the body, the first of which may be absent or only faintly visible in some specimens. The second blotch, the largest and most prominent in colour, is located just below the upper lateral line; the last blotch, second in intensity and size, lies on the caudal peduncle at the basis of the caudal fin.

Breeding pattern: Ground colour yellowish-white; first black blotch disappears and six black (not solid) vertical bars —rarely two merge and just five are evident— appear at the positions of the other blotches. A velvety black colour develops on the ventral area from the lips (including the lower lip) to the basis of the anal fin, including the ventral fins and the bases of the pectoral fins. The purple hue on the gill cover and cheek, as well as the salmon coloration of the anterior part of the dorsal fin, intensifies.

Preserved coloration

Body light brown, darkening in the head and dorsal area. Light spots on the unpaired fins. Seven black blotches on the posterior half of the body, the second one, the largest and most prominent, located just below the upper lateral line. The last blotch lies at the basis of the caudal fin and is second in intensity and size. In some females a dark blotch, with a size similar to the second blotch on the flank, is visible on the dorsal fin.

Material examined

Holotype: Museum of Zoology, University of Michigan: 221577. Adult male, 85.5 mm SL (109 mm total length), collected by the author using a casting net at "Las Cascadas" (99°23'47" W. Long., 21°56'47" N. Lat.) in the Río Tamasopo in April 1992.

Paratypes: Museum of Zoology, University of Michigan: 221829. One male, 78.5 mm SL (98.4 mm TL) and 5 females, 72.6, 78.4, 82.8, 83.0, and 86.9 mm SL (89.2, 98.1, 103.1, 105.6, and 109.2 mm TL respectively). Same collecting data as holotype.

Distribution and habitat

Herichthys tamasopoensis occurs in the mainstream and tributaries of the Río Gallinas, a Pánuco tributary which runs from an altitude of approximately 450 to 300 metres above sea level in the Sierra Madre Oriental. It is isolated from the Río Tampaón by the Tamul waterfall, a magnificent geological feature in the middle of the huesteca tropical forest. Measurements of water chemistry taken along this range show a general hardness that exceeds 100° DH and

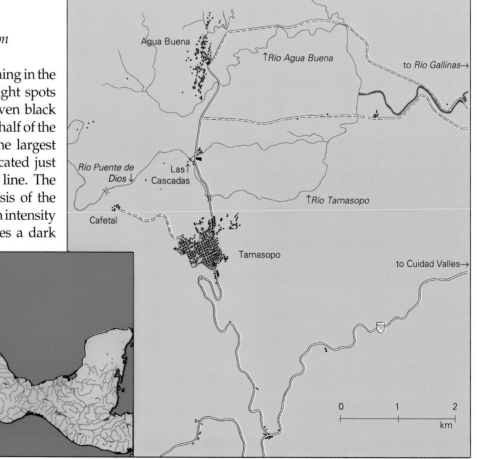

a pH varying from 7.8 to 8.3. The water is generally clear with a light blue to turquoise coloration, indicating the presence of large quantities of dissolved minerals. In the dry season visibility may be in excess of twenty metres in the headwaters of the Ríos Tamasopo and Ojo Frio. Visibility in the slower flowing waters of the Ríos Agua Buena and Gallinas is usually less than two metres. Water temperatures vary, with the Río Ojo Frio (the Spanish name refers to a cold spring) having the lowest in the range. Its highest temperature, during the dry months, is about 22° C. In the same season the temperature in the Ríos Tamasopo and Agua Buena may reach 28° C. The rainy season, which normally begins at the end of May and lasts till the end of October with peaks in July and September, not only reduces visibility to less than one metre over the whole range but also lowers temperatures to below 18° C.

There are no aquatic plants found in the Río Tamasopo. Only in the headwaters of the Río Ojo Frio, north of the village of Damian Carmona, can some plants be encountered, but no cichlids are found in this area.

In general the habitat of *H. tamasopoensis* is characterised by rocky bottoms that vary from large boulders to limestone sediments. The Río Gallinas with its tributaries forms a small basin with rivers varying in width from 5 to 30 metres. The depth of the river may sometimes be more than 15 metres (immediately below waterfalls) but generally is about two to three metres. The water flow varies from moderate to moderately fast. The surrounding vegetation consists of lush tropical forest with tall, more than 20 metres high, trees. Driftwood is commonly found on the river bottom. For environmental reasons, such as the cold water in the Río Ojo Frio, cichlids are not found over the whole range in the same density. Pollution caused by man is another reason for the unequal distribution of *H. tamasopoensis* in the Río Gallinas system. The badly treated wastes of a small sugar mill in Agua Buena have severely threatened aquatic life in the Río Agua Buena and near the town of Tambaca a huge mill, the "Alianza Popular", has completely extirpated aquatic life as far as the Tamul waterfall. This means that the major part of the natural range of *H. tamasopoensis* has been destroyed. Nevertheless, the Río Tamasopo holds a fish community that, in some places, can be as lively as that of a coral reef.

Ecology

Herichthys tamasopoensis shares its habitat with a number of other fishes. The livebearers include *Xiphophorus montezumae*, *Poecilia mexicana* and *Gambusia panuco*. In the headwaters of the Río Ojo Frio at "El Quince" *X. continens* is also found. Representatives of other fish families are *Astyanax fasciatus* (Characin), *Dionda* sp. (Cyprinid), and *Ictalurus mexicanus* (Catfish). Cichlids found together with *H. tamasopoensis* are *Nandopsis steindachneri* (not above the waterfalls at Tamasopo), *N.* cf. *labridens* (White Labridens), and *Oreochromis aureus* which has been introduced but which is very rare in the Ríos Tamasopo and Agua Buena.

At the end of the rainy season, around mid October, the water level in the river drops with a coincident increase in visibility and temperature. These factors stimulate algal growth on exposed surfaces and suddenly the emaciated fishes begin to change their appearance. Algae are the main food of *H. tamasopoensis* during the dry season and their presence makes the fishes look healthier and more colourful. Numerous groups of algae-grazing cichlids then form a common part of the underwater scenery. The structure of the teeth in *H. tamasopoensis* may be designed for the grazing of algae. Although it is decidedly herbivorous, I have sporadically witnessed this cichlid feeding on benthic invertebrates. Because of their different feeding habits the different species of cichlids live together in a state of mutual tolerance, even ignoring each other. *H. tamasopoensis* is normally found in water not deeper than two metres.

At the beginning of December the oxygen-rich zones near the waterfalls and cascades become the sites of breeding activity. Ripe males then start to develop nuchal humps and protect territories. The territory normally has some rocky surface included and, due to the high density of this species, is usually not larger than one metre in diameter. As soon as the males have become territorial females approach them and courting begins. After a pair is formed the breeding coloration appears in the male as well as the female. At this point interactions with neighbouring pairs, culminating in frontal displays with wide spread gill covers, are a common sight. However, such interactions seem to be restricted to display, and no damage is done. Mated couples are usually formed from males with a size between 11 and 15 cm and females with a length of 8 to 10 cm. Pairs smaller or larger than this are rare. Pairs generally favour a rocky crevice within the territory as spawning site. An area with a diameter of about 10 cm is cleaned by both fishes. About two to three hundred oval, yellowish-green, adhesive eggs with a length of about 2 mm along the long axis are placed in rows and kept well-oxygenated by fanning for a period of about two days, at the end of which they hatch. The wrigglers are transferred to one of several pre-dug pits which have a diameter as well as a depth of about 2 cm. Here they stay for about five days until the larvae have completely absorbed their yolk sacs and become freeswimming. Several hours later the fry, closely packed and guarded by the pair, start prospecting the immediate area around the pit for food. Both parents communicate with the fry by spasmodic movements of the body and by opening and closing of the fins. Fry move in a rotational arrangement in which the hindmost fry swim over the rest of the group in order to occupy a front position. The fry are rarely taken far away from the original spawning site. The fry forage on algae and detritus on tree leaves, rocks, and driftwood. When danger threatens they take refuge under leaves, wood, or stones. The female then takes position over them while the male disposes of the threat or, when this seems impossible, flees away (a common reaction in Central American cichlids, although *H. tamasopoensis* males seem to be more persistent in their defence). The fry enjoy their parents' protection until they have reached a length of about 2 cm. They eventually start venturing far from the territory and look for shelter in the shallow water near the banks where they are relatively protected against predators.

The breeding season peaks around February when hundreds of pairs can be observed caring for their fry. Towards the end of April the number of pairs has decreased significantly and becomes very low towards the end of May when the rains start falling over the huasteca forest.

Acknowledgements

I am very thankful to Martin Geerts, Mary Bailey, and Ad Konings for their valuable comments on an earlier version of the manuscript.

References

ALVAREZ del VILLAR, J. (1959) Nota preliminar sobre la Ictiofauna del estado de San Luis Potosí. *Acta Cient. Potosina*, Vol. III.
ALVAREZ del VILLAR, J. (1970) Peces Méxicanos (Claves). *Comisión Nacional Consultiva de Pesca.* pp 140-150.

ARTIGAS AZAS, J.M. (1990) The Tamasopo *Herichthys* Cichlid. *Buntb. Bull. (Am. Cichl. Assn.)* #137, pp 2-11.
BAIRD, S.F. & GIRARD, C. (1854) Descriptions of new species of fishes collected in Texas, New Mexico and Sonora, by Mr. John H. Clark, on the U.S. and Mexican Boundary Survey, and in Texas by Captain Stewart Van Vliet, U.S.A. *Proc. Acad. Nat. Sci. Philad.* 7, p 25.
BAREL, C.D.N., Van OIJEN, M.J.P., WITTE, F. & WITTE-MAAS, E.L.M. (1977) An introduction to the taxonomy and morphology of the Haplochromine cichlidae from Lake Victoria. *Neth. J. Zool.* 27(4), pp 333-389.
BURGESS, W.E. & WALLS, J.G. (1992) The name game. *Cichlasoma*: the next step. *Trop. Fish Hob.* Vol. 41 (5).
JORDAN, D.S., EVERMANN, B.W. & CLARK, H.B. (1930) Checklist of the fishes and fishlike vertebrates of North and Middle America, north of the northern boundary of Venezuela and Colombia. *Report U.S. Comm. Fish.*, pp 416-421.
JORDAN, D.S. & SNYDER, J.O. (1900) Notes on a collection of fishes from the rivers of Mexico, with descriptions of twenty new species. *Bull. U.S. Fish. Comm.* 19(1899), pp 115-147.
KULLANDER, S.O. (1983) *A revision of the South American cichlid genus Cichlasoma.* Swedish Mus. Nat. Hist. Stockholm.
KULLANDER, S.O. (1986) *Cichlid fishes of the Amazon river drainage of Peru.* Swedish Mus. Nat. Hist., Stockholm.
LOISELLE, P.V. (1982) Our national cichlid *Cichlasoma cyanoguttatum* Baird & Girard 1854. *FAMA.* May; pp 6-11/86-94.
MEEK, S.E. (1914) An annotated list of fishes known to occur in the fresh waters of Costa Rica. *Fieldiana, Zool. Ser.* 10; pp 101-134.
REGAN, C.T. (1905) A revision of the cichlids of the American genus *Cichlosoma* and of the allied genera. *Ann. Mag. Nat. Hist.*, ser. 7, vol. 16, pp 60-77; 225-243; 316-340; 433-445.
TAYLOR, J.N. & MILLER, R.R. (1983) Cichlid fishes (genus *Cichlasoma*) of the Rio Pánuco Basin, eastern Mexico, with description of a new species. *Occas. Pap. Mus. Nat. Hist. Univ. Kansas.* 104, pp 1-24.

Breeding pairs of *H. tamasopoensis* n. sp. under the waterfalls at Tamasopo with males showing nuchal humps at the beginning of the breeding season. Photo Juan Miguel Artigas.

Nandopsis loisellei (Bussing, 1989)

Willem Heijns

History

One of the first cichlids I kept was *Nandopsis managuense*; at least, I thought it was. Some years ago I was not the only one who applied that name to the species which is the subject of this article. The name *Cichlasoma managuense* was used in all available aquaristic publications with the exception of Robert Goldstein's book *"Cichlids of the world"*. In this book a photograph of *Nandospis managuense* showed a different species to the one with which I was familiar, but I regarded that as a mislabelled picture.

At the beginning of the eighties our German aquarist friends started their expeditions to Central America. One of them, Axel Mewes (Hannover), showed me a cichlid which he had collected in El Salvador and which he called *Petenia splendida*. Since El Salvador couldn't boast an extensive tourist industry I was glad that Axel gave me some of his fish. After a short acclimatisation I noticed that these cichlids showed a resemblance to the one in Goldstein's book. Realising that the name *Nandopsis managuense* was already "given to" another cichlid I thought that they must be a different species. When, however, the real *Petenia splendida* became available to

aquarists, it seemed that the cichlids from El Salvador had to be *Nandopsis managuense*. The cichlids which for years were known under the name *Nandopsis managuense* were then called *N. friedrichsthalii*. I have never understood why they chose this name .

A few years later a cichlid was imported from Belize and given the same name, namely *N. friedrichsthalii*. Initially this was regarded as a variant, but it was soon realised that this was incorrect. The differences between these two species were too prominent to be regarded as intraspecific variation. The type locality of *N. friedrichsthalii* was close enough to the collection site of the species from Belize for this cichlid to be now correctly known as *N. friedrichsthalii*. Consequently the species which many aquarists had kept for years and called *N. managuense* at one time and *N. friedrichsthalii* at another was now without a scientific name. And it remained without one for years.

Not until 1989 did our cichlid receive its scientific name. The famous Dr. William Bussing, who lives in Costa Rica, described this beautiful species as *Cichlasoma loisellei*, named after Dr. Paul Loiselle, a very well known American cichlid specialist. A remarkable feature of this

A male *Nandopsis managuense* from El Salvador.

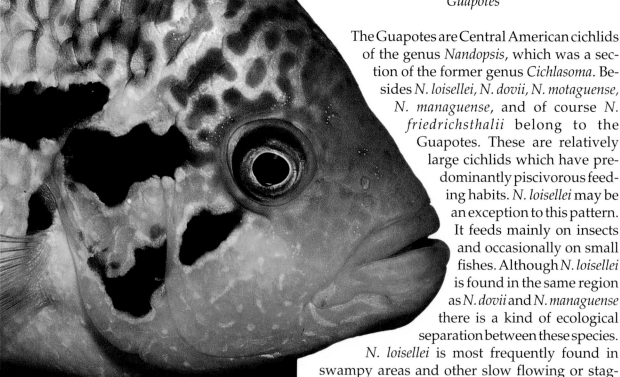

The Guapotes are Central American cichlids of the genus *Nandopsis*, which was a section of the former genus *Cichlasoma*. Besides *N. loisellei, N. dovii, N. motaguense, N. managuense,* and of course *N. friedrichsthalii* belong to the Guapotes. These are relatively large cichlids which have predominantly piscivorous feeding habits. *N. loisellei* may be an exception to this pattern. It feeds mainly on insects and occasionally on small fishes. Although *N. loisellei* is found in the same region as *N. dovii* and *N. managuense* there is a kind of ecological separation between these species.

Nandopsis loisellei, a male. Photo Willem Heijns.

description is that Bussing completely ignores the usage "*Cichlasoma*" (with quotation marks) which was proposed in Kullander's revision of the genus *Cichlasoma* and which was mentioned in Bussing's reference list. We will follow Lucena & Kullander (1992: 149) and use *Nandopsis*.

N. loisellei is most frequently found in swampy areas and other slow flowing or stagnant waters with a muddy bottom. *N. dovii* prefers the somewhat faster flowing water and is usually found in the middle of streams and rivers and in lakes. *N. managuense* is normally found in lakes.

There is a close relationship between *N. loisellei* and *N. friedrichsthalii*. They could be sister species, i.e. species with a common ancestor. Evidence in support of this relationship may be

A pair *Nandopsis loisellei*. Photo Willem Heijns.

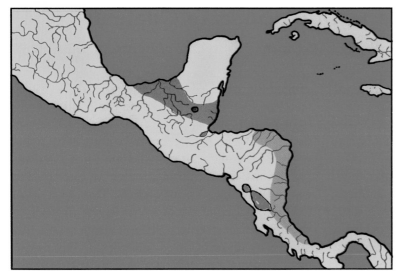

The distribution of *N. friedrichsthalii* (red) and *N. loisellei* (green).

of the ancestral species, now *N. friedrichsthalii* and *N. loisellei*, could have contact once again. It is thus possible that an area exists in which these species are sympatric.

Nandopsis loisellei in the aquarium

My experiences with this species go back a long time. I maintained a pair of *N. loisellei* in an aquarium of 500 litres (200x50x50 cm). The male was 25 cm and the female a little smaller. In my experience paired Guapotes are the easiest fish to keep provided enough room is made available for them. The pair spawned regularly and produced hundreds of fry. These fry I left to the care of the parents because I could then admire their guarding behaviour. Nevertheless, the presence of *Neetroplus nematopus* in the same tank took care of over-population. Because of their relatively small size *N. nematopus* were able to steal the fry and return to their cave before the parents could take action against them. It took them about four days to steal a complete spawn of *N. loisellei*, which usually numbers about 800 fry.

N. loisellei is not sensitive to the quality of the water and will eat any type of food provided it is administered in adequate quantities.

Nandopsis friedrichsthalii.

Nandopsis motaguense, a female.

Nandopsis motaguense, a male. Photos Willem Heijns.

derived from their distribution patterns (see map). It is not known to which of the two species the Guapotes inhabiting the region between the two distribution areas belong. This intermediate region was previously part of the Amatique Basin. This was a sea-arm extending deep into Central American land and formed a barrier to the spreading of the freshwater fauna. After the basin dried up and rivers were created the two populations

Reference

LUCENA, C.A.S. & KULLANDER, S.O. (1992) The *Crenicichla* (Teleostei: Cichlidae) species of the Uruguai River drainage in Brazil. *Ichth. Expl. Freshw.* Vol. 3 (2): pp 97-160.

Observations on *Herichthys pearsei* in Guatemala.

Jaap-Jan de Greef

Herichthys pearsei belongs to a group of *"Cichlasomas"* of which the best known species is the so-called Texas Cichlid, *H. cyanoguttatum*, with three subspecies. The species in the genus *Herichthys* are distinguished from other *"Cichlasomas"* by the structure of their teeth, which indicates a major emphasis on the vegetable element of their diet. They have a row of teeth protruding from their lips used for grazing vegetation from rocks and submerged wood, roots and branches. I first came upon a member of this group when I travelled with a group of archaeologists through northern Guatemala. We camped on the banks of the river Usumacinta near Yaxchilan. We had eaten frijoles (beans) for almost three straight weeks and I was getting tired of beans with corn tortillas. In order to add variety to our menu, I

angled for fish using tortilla as bait. It wasn't very successful as most of the time the tortillas were being eaten off the hook by tetras (*Astyanax mexicanus*) which are extremely abundant in this region. However, all of a sudden I got a serious pull on my line and I reeled in what appeared to me to be a huge Texas Cichlid. The fish was at least a foot long and it was a welcome addition to the beans that evening. I didn't come across this species again until I was collecting fish in northern Guatemala in 1983. As I was inquiring about the different kinds of fishes in the area, people kept mentioning a large yellow fish that they referred to as "Querudo". "Quero" is the Spanish word for leather, and the reason they call this fish "leatherlike" is that its skin is a lot tougher than that of other cichlids in the area, making it harder

A fisherman casting his net on the Río Sayaxché, Petén District. Inset: Río de la Pasión, habitat of *Herichthys pearsei*. Photos Jaap-Jan de Greef.

A freshly caught *Herichthys pearsei*. Photos Jaap-Jan de Greef.

to clean. I wondered what this fish was because I prefer to collect juveniles on my trips, as their survival rate is much higher and one can take a few more fishes back. The natives told me that juveniles look very much like another ubiquitous cichlid from the Río de la Pasión/Usumacinta drainage, namely *"Cichlasoma" synspilum*, popularly known as the "Quetzal Cichlid". The Querudo would be found where thick vegetation hangs over and in the water, thus making it difficult to throw a cast net to catch them. I was unsuccessful in catching either adults or juveniles, but later that year, when I returned a second time, I discovered how the natives catch them. They collect a little tomato-like berry from a plant that grows wild in the Petén region (the northernmost province of Guatemala). The berries are put on small hooks and thrown near thickets of a bamboo-like grass with razorsharp leaves, the reason for the fishes' thick skin. The fishes readily go for the berries. They reminded me of the Pacu in the Amazonas region of South America, a tetra which specialises in a similar strategy in the flooded forest. The Usumacinta, and especially the Río de la Pasión, behaves like a mini-Amazonas, where the river floods during the rainy season and trees drop their fruit into the water and in this manner seed themselves around. The fishes eat the fruit and the seeds pass through their digestive systems, aiding the dispersal of the tree. Areas where the Querudo occurs are often hard to observe under water. They tend to live in the murky parts of the river, making it hard to observe breeding pairs with fry in the wild. It also makes it more

difficult to bring back young fishes as one of the best ways to bring back cichlids in reasonable numbers is to rob part of a nest. Whenever I collect cichlids I rob a few fry from different breeding pairs whenever possible so as to guarantee a wider gene pool with which to start a captive population.

Herichthys pearsei is a beautiful fish, but unfortunately its large size will always limit it in the hobby to the very few who have ample space and the desire to keep a long-living species such as this. The species is currently available from a few fish farms in Florida and hopefully will get around enough so that its interesting behaviour can be studied in more detail.

Note the berries with which the Querudo was hooked.

Thorichthys callolepis Regan, 1904

Ad Konings

A pool in the Río Grande near Puente Ajal. This is the locality where the photographs were taken.

The drainage area of the upper Coatzacoalcos, which lies in the southwestern part of the Istmo de Tehuantepec (Isthmus of Tehuantepec) in the Mexican state Oaxaca, consists of several small rivers inhabited by at least six different species of cichlids. About 10 km south of Matias Romero federal route 185 crosses a small river which is named Río Grande on three different Mexican maps but is often referred to as Río Almoloya in literature. The temperature of the water during our visit in March was 28° C, the pH 8.0, and total hardness 14° DH. At Puente Ajal the river has an average width of about 5 metres and an average depth of about 50 cm. In some places the water cascades over a rocky dam and widens into a pool after such obstacle. One such pool had a maximum depth of about three metres and was about 10 metres across. The visibility was rather good; fishes could be seen several metres away. The flow of the water was moderate, especially through the pool. The bottom was sandy although there was quite a lot of mud despite the current. In the deeper parts of the pool the bottom was covered with a thick layer of tree leaves, a common substrate in Mexican rivers. Rocks, small

A *Thorichthys callolepis* in neutral dress.

and medium sized, alternated with tree-stumps and roots in the shallower areas of the pool.

Two cichlid species are endemic to the upper Coatzacoalcos: *"Cichlasoma" regani* and *Thorichthys callolepis*. In the Río Grande (Matias Romero) —in Mexico there are more than 25 rivers and villages named Río Grande— the latter species lives sympatrically with *Thorichthys helleri. T. helleri*, in the upper Coatzacoalcos, is characterised by a red coloration on the lower half of the head sprinkled with blue spots. Quiescent females have a large black spot, demarcated with a whitish-

A fry-guarding male *Thorichthys callolepis*; some fry are visible near the pelvic fins.

A female T. callolepis guarding fry.

blue edging, in the dorsal fin. Fry-guarding *T. helleri* have a pattern of vertical bars on an almost white body.

The main characteristic that sets *T. callolepis* apart from *T. helleri* (and all other species of *Thorichthys*) is the lack of a black spot on the gillcover.

Besides the three species mentioned *"Cichlasoma" guttatum*, *"C". salvini* and *Paraneetroplus bulleri* were also observed in the Río Grande. The most abundant fish, however, was the tetra *Astyanax fasciatus*. An important part of the tetra's diet consists of cichlid fry; a school of tetras can be a real nuisance to a fry-guarding cichlid.

Thorichthys callolepis—*callolepis* means "with beautiful scales"— lives mainly in the deeper parts of the Río Grande where it forages on the bottom,

picking bits and pieces from the leaves that litter the substrate. No difference was observed in the feeding techniques of *T. callolepis* and *T. helleri*. Both species could be found side by side feeding from the same substrate. *T. helleri* must have been dominating *T. callolepis* in some way because there were approximately 100 times more *T. helleri* than *T. callolepis*.

Male *T. callolepis* have a maximum size of about 11cm (TL); females, with a maximum size of approximately 7cm, are much smaller. The sizes of the sympatric *T. helleri* were similar.

We observed only three breeding pairs of *T. callolepis* of which only one pair were defending eggs; the other two pairs were taking care of fry. The eggs of the former pair were deposited on a small rock rather exposed to the outside world. Many brooding pairs of *T. helleri* were seen but their broods were more or less concealed from the outside world. Both species guard their fry close to the nest and do not lead them through the habitat. The fry forage from the sediment on the leaves and sand. Fry-guarding *T. helleri* have a zebra-type coloration pattern whereas breeding *T. callolepis* lose most of the pinkish orange colour on the lower part of their body. The spawn sizes varied between 50 and 100 fry for both species.

The apparent success of *T. helleri* compared to *T. callolepis* may be due to the better protection of the

Thorichthys helleri, here a female, is sympatric with *T. callolepis*.

eggs and fry in the former. The tetra would probably not taste any difference between these two cichlids' eggs, but since *T. callolepis* eggs are more exposed to the outside world they run a higher risk of being eaten than those of *T. helleri*.

T. callolepis has been introduced, on a small scale, in the hobby and will hopefully be available in the near future. Its pastel coloration, small size, and interesting behaviour are the right ingredients for a serious cichlid-lover.

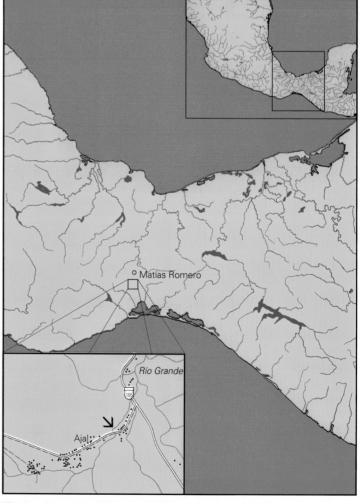

The locality visited (Puente Ajal) is indicated with an arrow.

SOUTH AMERICAN CICHLIDS

Some remarks on the identification of
Crenicichla lenticulata Heckel, 1840

Frank Warzel

The so-called "large *Crenicichla*" group contains a whole series of species with striking display coloration or attractive markings. Even "grey mice" such as, for example, *Crenicichla* sp. "Strigata" from Venezuela, have an extremely vivid pattern of spots and longitudinal bands as juveniles, and for this reason are imported more frequently than

peduncle, somewhat above the median line of the body, runs a straight line of almost rectangular spots of irregular outline, 8 on one side of the body and 9 on the other; these are more than an eye diameter in width and are positioned close together....."; also: "Beneath this row of large spots, through which runs the upper lateral line, there is

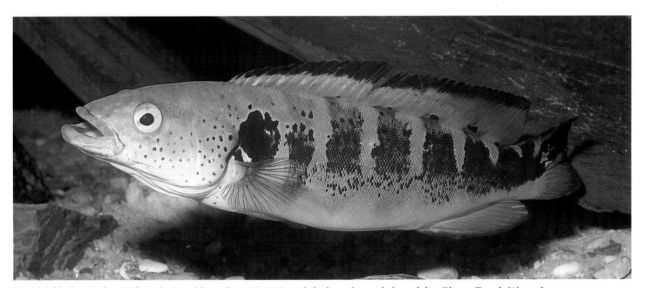

Crenicichla lenticulata, a female (total length *ca* 23 cm) with light coloured dorsal fin. Photo Frank Warzel.

might otherwise be the case. But this group also contains species which develop an intense black pattern as adults. These include *C. marmorata* and also the very closely related *C. lenticulata*. Like in *C. marmorata*, *C. lenticulata* appears to be a highly variable species. Our first live specimens, seen in Colombia, were so sparsely patterned that at first we thought we were dealing with an undescribed *Crenicichla*. Surprisingly, a few of the juveniles we brought back developed a pattern like that which Heckel described for *C. lenticulata* in the year 1840: "From the shoulder girdle to the caudal

a whole mass of smaller, but at the same time blacker, spots which in every case cover no more than a single scale......"
Why all the Orinoco-specimens over 30 cm —also from different localities— have a pattern of markings which is only faintly reminiscent of Heckel's description is a question which must remain unanswered for the time being. Although we cannot be absolutely positive, the fact that our aquarium specimens have a distinctive patterning argues against the superficial view that they are perhaps a geographical variety. Moreover it was

the experience of Uwe Werner and his companions last year, during their expedition to the Rio Uaupés, a tributary of the upper Rio Negro, that individual *C. lenticulata* can be extremely variable in their patterning. While one fish was covered uniformly in small black spots, another had such spots only in the region of the stripes on the back. On the other hand specimens from widely separated localities may apparently be very similar in

A juvenile *C. lenticulata* (total length *ca* 11 cm) from Río Atabapo, Colombia. Photo Frank Warzel.

however, major differences in the patterning of juveniles, as 8 cm long, approximately 3 to 4 months old, *C. lenticulata* have no pattern of longitudinal bands while these are typical of *C. marmorata* juveniles and juveniles of other closely related species. Instead at a very early stage bands are apparent on the back, and these, in contrast to the case in adult specimens, are clearly thickened. The thickening of these bars lies along a slightly downcurved line and produces a chain-like pattern. Additional characters in juvenile *C. lenticulata* from the Río Atabapo and from the Caño Bocon are a narrow stripe in front of and behind the eye, as well as yellow-bordered, relatively large, dorsal spots, although the first-mentioned character is typical of other closely related species as well. Apropos of which, there is a phenomenon worth noting: the number and intensity of the spots on the head appears to alter several times as the fish grows, and may even sometimes completely disappear. It remains to be seen whether this phenomenon applies equally to all *C. lenticulata*. An observation by Natterer, quoted by Heckel —"The black spots on the head may disappear at spawning time."— was confirmed by a large breeding pair of *C. lenticulata* observed in the Caño Bocon near Puerto Inirida. Of course Natterer's observation does in fact refer to *Crenicichla adspersa* Heckel 1840 from the Río Guaporé, which is regarded as a separate species in the revision of *Crenicichla* by Ploeg (1991). In the same work *Crenicichla ornata* Regan 1905, which was described from half-grown specimens, is synonymised with *C. lenticulata*. According to Ploeg the majority of localities for *C. lenticulata* lie in the Rio Negro, the upper Rio Branco, and the upper Rupununi River. The species is, however, not uncommon in both the Río Atabapo and the Río Inirida as well. This, together with the existence of a locality in the lower Amazonas, gives *C. lenticulata* a relatively wide distribution. It would certainly be interesting to keep *C. lenticulata* from other localities in the aquarium, as the observations made so far provide only a limited view of a species which is so far hardly known in the hobby.

pattern. Thus the description of the specimens seen by Heckel, which came from the upper Rio Negro near Marabitanas, matches very closely a large pair of *C. lenticulata* which Heiko Bleher caught in the Amazonas some 150 km downstream of Manaus. A large male, which likewise very closely resembles Heckel's description, is pictured on page 263 of Stawikowski & Werner (1988).

Obviously there can be difficulties in the identification of species which are highly variable in their patterning. And the most recent revision of *Crenicichla* by Alex Ploeg offers only the scantiest information on this subject. On the basis of existing knowledge, however, *C. marmorata* is basically the only species which can be confused with *C. lenticulata*, although typical specimens of the two species are easily differentiated. In contrast to the case in *C. marmorata*, in *C. lenticulata* the light areas separating the bands on the back always extend as far as the dorsal fin and do not have dark edges. Moreover *C. lenticulata* has a more or less bold pattern of spots on these bands or along the axis of the body. As far as morphometrics are concerned, meristic differences are restricted to a few details, and here too there may be overlap. Interestingly there are,

Crenicichla cametana Steindachner, 1911 and C. jegui Ploeg, 1986

Frank Warzel

Of the 80 known species of *Crenicichla*, some of which remain undescribed, *C. cametana* and in particular *C. jegui* must surely be considered among the most noteworthy representatives of the genus. Both are extremely well adapted to their biotope, their habitat being restricted mainly to rocky formations in rapids and fast-flowing stretches of water. The extreme degree of adaptation to the rocky biotope is without doubt one of the reasons that *C. cametana* and *C. jegui* are endemic to the Rio Tocantins and the Rio Araguaia, and for their distribution remaining restricted to this clear water river system. The unusual, and—as far as the specialised and hardly researched fish fauna is concerned— less than welcome situation brought about by the imminent completion of a damming project led to the collection there, at the beginning of the 1980s, of numerous fishes by the staff of the "Instituto Nacional de Pesquisas da Amazonia", INPA for short. Among these fishes were found several unknown *Crenicichlas*. Now it may be years, or even decades, before such new discoveries can be

studied and made generally known. But in this case it was quite different. A relatively short time later the species discovered there were determined by the Dutch *Crenicichla* specialist Alex Ploeg and four new species described: *C. astroblepa*, *C. compressiceps*, *C. cyclostoma*, and *C. jegui*. As it happened this work contained many mis-identifications, which Ploeg corrected in 1991 after more extensive researches. Thus it transpired that almost all the characters of the species described by him as *C. astroblepa* overlapped those of another *Crenicichla* species which was already known. Since then further collections have suggested that *C. astroblepa* should be regarded as a synonym of *C. cametana* Steindachner 1911. One reason for the apparent failure to recognise the identity of the two species must be the differing body proportions, which alter in the course of the growth of the fish. The three specimens which form the type series of *C. cametana*, all adult fishes, originated from the lower Tocantins near to the town of Cametá, while those of *C. astroblepa* were obtained somewhat

Shallow rocky biotope in the Rio Araguaia near São Bento; the habitat of *C. cametana* and *C. jegui*. Photo Frank Warzel.

A male *C. cametana* with a total length of about 20 cm. Photos Frank Warzel.

further upstream at Tucuruí, Jatobal, and Caperuana. Ploeg (1991) also mentions a locality in the Rio das Mortes on the upper Araguaia. Not that this precludes the possibility of *C. cametana* also inhabiting the upper reaches of this river system. But the brief description of coloration given by Ploeg leaves room for doubt as to whether he referred to *C. astroblepa* or to another species which is similar in body shape but not in coloration. In my personal experience only *C. jegui* and this, very closely related and undescribed, species have double cross-bands on the back or along the axis of the body. *C. cametana* is certainly found in the lower Rio Araguaia at São Bento, but from my personal observations appears to be a little

less common there. *C. cametana*, like *C. jegui*, shows several morphological peculiarities. In the genus *Crenicichla* we can see two basically contrasting adaptations in form. While small rheophilic species, for example *C. compressiceps* and *C. cyclostoma*, are laterally compressed, *C. cametana* and also *C. jegui* have dorsally compressed bodies compared to those of other species. Both types of adaptation appear to be related to lifestyle, allowing optimised utilisation of particular food sources. Although to date there have been no investigations of stomach contents, it is very probable, on account of the narrow mouth and relatively short jaws, that the laterally compressed types such as *C. cyclostoma* and *C.*

Crenicichla jegui, a young male.

compressiceps are specialised in feeding mainly on small invertebrates such as insect larvae and snails. *C. cametana* and *C. jegui*, by contrast, live an extremely predatory existence and in nature probably feed mainly on fishes. In the aquarium they have been observed to overwhelm suitably sized food fishes measuring up to more than three quarters of their own body length. But there are significant differences in the lifestyles of the two species, connected with, among other factors, their differing swimming capabilities. While *C. cametana*, in spite of its very bottom-oriented way of life, can maintain a position in open water in the aquarium without difficulty, in *C. jegui* this is possible only by means of strong, rather clumsy, movements. Totally atrophied and thus non-functional swimbladders are by no means unusual in a number of rheophilous cichlids, but in the

A female *Crenicichla cametana* with breeding coloration.

Crenicichla genus, however, this is the exception. As can be seen in the natural habitat, this apparently clumsy mode of swimming in short bursts is far from useless against a current, as *C. jegui* can normally only be caught in its hiding place, to which it periodically returns. In nature, and also in the aquarium, *C. jegui* spends much of its time under rocks and flat stones, preferring to rest with its snout, as far as the eyes, protruding in order to see what is happening outside its hiding place. *C. cametana* and *C. cyclostoma* likewise live almost exclusively under stones in their natural habitat, but in contrast to *C. jegui* appear even more inclined to remain in hiding and are far more sedentary. At any rate they have not been seen to cover long distances in flight. The clearly differently specialised predators *C. cametana* and

C. jegui undoubtedly utilise a variety of food sources. In this respect *C. jegui*, far more than *C. cametana*, embodies the typical active lurking predator, which lurks almost motionless, but ever on the lookout for prey, outside its hiding place. Active in this case means that it does not rely on its cryptic coloration and wait until the potential prey is so near to its mouth that it has only to open the latter and "inhale" the prey. Instead the eyes, which are positioned very high on the head, and which can be directed slightly upwards, make it far more likely that *C. jegui* has specialised in the capture of fishes in the upper water layers, or at the very least those which swim past at some distance from its lair. Although aquarium life imposes restrictions on natural behaviour, it can be observed that *C. jegui* always seizes prey fishes or pieces of food during quick sallies, and then, successful or not, invariably returns to its lair after the attack. With regard to suitable companions, it must be noted that *C. jegui* may attack relatively large tankmates and regards these as potential items of prey. The specialisation is so far developed that mosquito larvae and other small frozen foods are as good as ignored by adult specimens. As already indicated, *C. cametana* is somewhat less extreme in this respect. But its ability to gulp down even very large food fishes, together with its relatively strongly enlarged, conical, and backwards-pointing teeth, lead to the assumption that *C. cametana* must also be extremely predatory in its feeding habits. Possibly this species specialised at an early stage in feeding on those fishes which prefer to live a concealed existence or are more substrate-oriented. Moreover the two species differ in the development of their jaw dentition. In contrast to that of *C. cametana*, the dentition of *C. jegui* extends very much further into the gullet region. There are only a very few *Crenicichla* species which possess this type of enlarged teeth. Almost without exception they are members of the so-called *C. reticulata* group, which were at one time even segregated into a separate genus. In addition the species of this former genus, *Batrachops* Heckel 1840, have fewer rows of teeth than other *Crenicichlas*. Ploeg (1991) included *C. cametana* and *C. cyclostoma* in this group. *C. jegui*, on the other hand, was placed in the group of very large *Crenicichlas* closely related to *C. lugubris*. This was mainly on account of its relatively high scale counts. But looked at critically, and taking into account the other numerical data, *C. jegui* lies at the bottom limit of variation within the group. In addition the pattern of d o u b l e stripes, as well as the courtship dress of the female, suggests that *C. jegui* is in fact another *"Batrachops"*. As in *C. cametana* and *C. cyclostoma*, at certain times female *C. jegui* develop an intense red band on the upper edge of the dorsal. This is less well defined along its lower edge and extends a bit more into the spinous part of the fin. It is worth noting that only the species endemic to the Rio Tocantins, namely *C. cyclostoma*, *C. cametana*, and *C. jegui*, have a similar courtship dress. In all other species observed in the aquarium to date there is a bright red, or sometimes orange, band in the middle or lower part of the dorsal fin. But *C. jegui* and another species, which may also inhabit the Rio Tocantins, share a character which is to date unknown in other members of *"Batrachops"*. The oblique stripe beneath the eye seems to be more likely a characteristic feature of another closely r e l a t e d group, the *C. l a c u s t r i s* group, and these species also may develop a similar pattern. Continuing scientific researches, or observations of further species from what is so far

a group largely unknown to aquarists, may perhaps throw further light on this matter.

Top: *C. jegui*; below: *C. cametana*. Photos Frank Warzel.

References

PLOEG, A. (1986) The cichlid genus *Crenicichla* from the Tocantins River, state of Pará, Brazil, with descriptions of four new species. *Beaufortia* (36) 5: pp 57-80.
PLOEG, A. (1991) *Revision of the South American cichlid genus* Crenicichla *Heckel, 1840, with descriptions of fifteen new species and considerations on species groups, phylogeny and biogeography*. (Dissertation) University of Amsterdam.
REGAN, C.T. (1905) A revision of the fishes of the South-American cichlid genera *Crenacara*, *Batrachops* and *Crenicichla*. *Proc. zool. Soc. London*.: pp 152-168.
STEINDACHNER, F. (1911) Über einige neue seltene südamerikanischen Süßwasserfische. *Anz. Akad. Wiss. Wien*. (48): pp 369-376.
STAWIKOWSKI, R. & WARZEL, F. (1991) Jacundá do Tocantins. *DATZ* 44 (8): pp 517-519 and 44 (9): pp 575-581.

Colombia, a paradise for cichlidophiles.
Part 1: Collecting *Pterophyllum altum*.

Kaj Andersen

It is terribly warm here; the sweat runs down into the eyes to the enjoyment of various kinds of colourful mosquitos and other vampire-like flying creations, among which some fearsome 2 cm-long flies are especially noteworthy. These very quickly attack you and before you realise what has happenend you are missing a few millimetres of sun-tanned skin from your leg; it is quite painful. Maybe you will ask yourself what you are doing in such a place. However, it is very simple to answer that question: it is unbelievably nice! A real jungle with a voluptuous growth of green plants which have flowers in all the colours you can imagine. Looking up into the trees you see orchids and bromeliads, lots of them, many with gorgeous red and yellow flowers. Even higher up, in the tops of the trees, there are colourful parrots climbing around and jumping from branch to branch. When you look down to the jungle floor you notice fantastic creations belonging to the creeping insect world. Very prominent are the leaf-cutting ants, each carrying an, in relation to its own size, enormous piece of foliage between its mandibles. Yes, the life here is fantastic, but the real reason we are here is because of the interesting streams in which are found some of the most exciting fishes which are representatives of the South American cichlids. In this article I will concentrate on two quite different biotopes. The first biotope is situated in east Colombia in a tributary of the Río Inirida, called Caño Joaquin. It is a small stream with rather strong current. The water has the colour of breakfast tea. It is especially interesting to see this tea-coloured water flow into the Río Inirida which is a white water river. The immediate surroundings of the Caño Joaquin are unbelievably beautiful: it has chalk-white banks, abundant plant growth and remarkably clear water, in which we were able to observe many interesting fishes. In February and March, in the dry season, the roots of the trees jut out of the water and bear clear markings showing the water level during the rainy season, about five metres high! As soon as we arrived at this spot we wanted to observe the fishes more closely. The excitement of looking under water equaled that above water. We saw hundreds of differ-

The light coloured rocks are clearly visible in the tea-coloured water of the Caño Joaquin. Photo Kaj Andersen.

The roots in the habitat of *P. altum* make collecting with a net almost impossible. Photos Kaj Andersen.

namely *Pterophyllum altum*. This is one of the few cichlids which are not yet bred in captivity. One of our goals was to find out this cichlid's natural habitat. In order to obtain some specimens we draped our large net around some roots where we had spotted some *P. altum*. We quickly found out that it was impossible to raise the net because pieces of root were caught in it, but after an hour of hard labour we managed to chase a *P. altum* into the net. After we had carefully disentangled the fish we brought it ashore and placed it in a plastic container. Some aquarists think that the discus is the king of the cichlids but after having seen the majestic *P. altum* one easily has second thoughts. Our collection of high-finned angel fishes consisted of about 25 fish of which the biggest was 33 cm high! The extended rays in the caudal, pelvic

ent tetras and catfishes. Among them were some large, 10 to 15 cm, beautiful *Mesonauta insignis* with a sunshine yellow colour and numerous red spots all over the body. Small and large representatives of *Satanoperca acuticeps* and *S. daemon* were also observed. The most abundant cichlid was *Biotodoma wavrini*. They were present in incredible numbers; half of the fishes caught with our nets were *B. wavrini*. Of course there were many tree roots in the river, both those of dead trees and rotten roots from trees that were still alive. Among the network of roots we found one of the cichlids we were especially interested in, and anal fin were more than 10 cm long! Later on during our trip we found *P. altum* at several other localities. Each time they were shoaling together in groups of about 10 to 30 individuals. All the individuals of *P. altum* we were able to observe were 25 cm or larger. We did not see any juveniles. My theory is that juveniles gather in large schools, numbering well over a thousand individuals, and forage in the main river. This theory was confirmed by a local fishman who had collected ornamental fishes in the native waters of *P. altum* before. According to the local fisherman *P. altum* breeds when the rainy season starts. It is during this period that a huge amount of fresh water runs down into the river providing a lot of food. When the juveniles have reached a size of approximately 3 to 4 cm they migrate in large schools from the breeding grounds to the deeper water of the main river. The advantage to a small fish of travelling in large schools is obvious. One point that clearly confirms this theory is the fact that the indians, shortly after the rains have stopped, collect large numbers of juvenile *P. altum* in relatively deep water of the main river.

The water in the Caño Joaquin had the following qualities: pH 4.8, total hardness 0°, carbonate hardness 4°, no measurable nitrite, a conductivity of 15 μS/cm, and a temperature of 30° C. The air temperature at 14.00hr was 33°C. If you wish to keep and possibly breed *P. altum* in an aquarium you should take into account several essential factors. One requirement is that the tank must be large and, in particular, deep. Fishes with the enormous height we found in wild specimens in Colombia need plenty of room. Undoubtedly *P. altum* can attain an even greater height, even in aquaria. Another factor that may need to be taken into consideration is the observation that *P. altum* lives in large groups among a network of roots.

A gorgeous *Pterophyllum altum*. Photo Kaj Andersen.

part 2: The Choco province

I would like to talk about a biotope in Colombia which is situated in the western part between the Cordillera Occidental mountain range and the Pacific Ocean. The Cordillera Occidental is part of the northern Andes. Colombia is divided into several small districts, one of which, Choco, we visited. The wildlife is different from that in East Colombia because the jungle here is much denser and impassable. Roads are scarce and if you find one it is gravel with numerous potholes. Road signs are very much conspicuous by their absence; so if you travel in this part of Colombia you need to be lucky to find the right way. The richness of the vegetation in the jungle, however, is incredible. In one square metre of the jungle you can find more than 100 different plants, each one of them with gorgeous flowers. I was especially enthralled by the many different species of terrestrial orchids. Also the creeping and flying insects, especially the butterflies, were something special. The locals are very dark skinned and direct descendents of the African slaves that the Spaniards brought here some centuries ago. They were very helpful and we owe them a lot of gratitude for their efforts.

Aquaristically seen this part of Colombia is very exciting because there are no commercial fish collecting stations. All the fishes caught in the rivers end up over the fire, and I must admit, they taste very good. The only way to obtain some of the fishes native to the West Colombian rivers and streams is to catch them yourself. In all the streams we visited we found fish that we had never seen before. One of the cichlids we wanted to collect was *Geophagus pellegrini*. Of course we had done a lot of investigation before we started this trip. We had found out where Mr. G. Palmer in 1909 had collected the three specimens which

are stored in the British Museum (Natural History) in London. On the basis of these three specimens Regan in 1912 described *Geophagus pellegrini*. Palmer caught the specimens in the Río San Juan near the village of Tado (Choco province). We went to the same locality but even after a careful investigation we succeeded in collecting only some specimens of *"Cichlasoma" atromaculatum* which also is a very attractive looking cichlid. We were convinced that *Geophagus pellegrini* must be somewhere nearby. So, in the following days all the streams that we encountered were carefully investi-

Some streams in the Choco province contain crystal clear water. Photo Kaj Andersen.

gated. Our base was at the Hotel Residencial Orsan in the village of Istmina. While showing a photograph we asked everybody if they had seen such a fish or if they knew anybody who could take us to a stream where we might find it. But to no avail. One day we tried our luck in the Río Quito, which is a tributary of the Río Atrato. Before we reached the Río Quito we passed a small tributary which had a width of about 5 metres and looked very interesting. We were lucky. In this little stream we observed, for the first time, live *Geophagus pellegrini*. The large males had fantastic coloration and the larger ones an enormous hump on the head. These humps were much bigger than we had ever seen in *Geophagus steindachneri*. The largest males measured about 25 to 30 cm; the adult females, which lacked most of the beautiful coloration seen in the male, were about 15 to 20 cm. We found that the large adult *G. pellegrini* swam around in small groups of about 10 individuals. The smaller individuals were mostly seen foraging solitary between the stones and roots on the bottom. We managed to collect some of the smaller individuals which are now swimming in several aquaria in Scandinavia. We think that the name of the stream where we collected *G. pellegrini* is Río Tirado because it runs close to the village of that name.

Besides *G. pellegrini* we also collected *"C." atromaculatum*, *Poecilia chocoensis*, and many different kinds of catfishes. The characteristics of the water in the Río Tirado are as follows: pH 6.8, total and carbonate hardness not measurable, conductivity 24 µS/cm, temperature 28° C, air temperature in the shade 29° C, and in the sun 37° C.

Geophagus pellegrini is an ovophilous mouthbrooder. A spawning is preceded by the male stationing himself with erected fins in front of the female while shaking his entire body. Sometimes it looks as if the male "vacuum cleans" the bottom with his mouth. Thereafter the female finds a stone or root which is cleaned of algae and sediment. The pair first start circling around and then the female lays one to three eggs at a time on the chosen spot. These are fertilised by the male at the same moment as the female takes them into her mouth. This spawning technique is similar to that of *G. steindachneri*. Mouthbrooding lasts about 14 days after which the fry are released. They have a length of about 10 mm and can eat newly hatched *Artemia* nauplii and *Cyclops*.

Our hunt for *G. pellegrini* one day led us to the Río Condoto. We quickly found out that this river is too big and too dirty to snorkel. When we returned we found a small stream which

Geophagus pellegrini, a sub-adult in the author's aquarium. Photo F. Ingemann Hansen.

was probably a tributary of the Río Condoto. This stream was very clear, had a width of about 5 metres, and was approximately one metre deep. When we tried our luck here we found several cichlids but no *G. pellegrini*. We were able to collect, however, *"C." atromaculatum*, an *"Aequidens"* species (possibly *"Ae." sapayensis*), some catfishes of the genera *Ancistrus* and *Loricaria*, the livebearer *Pseudopoecilia nigroventralis*, plus a very interesting and nice looking *"Aequidens" biseriatus*. During our trip we found the latter species at several other places as well. Regan described *"Ae." biseriatus* (as *Cichlasoma biseriatum*) in 1930 from specimens collected in the Río Condoto. (The current correct taxonomic placement of this cichlid is unclear therefore quotation marks are used to indicate this.) *"Ae." biseriatus* males attain a length of about 17 cm; females remain some centimetres smaller. The only external distinction between the sexes is the better developed fins of the male. The basic colour of the fish is golden brown. It has a yellowish coloured head with some bright blue markings —also common in other *Aequidens*. The coloration turns to very dark when *"Ae." biseriatus* is breeding.

The map shows the localities mentioned.

"Ae." biseriatus is a substrate brooder. In my tank the female always deposited the eggs on the side of the same stone. Both male and female guard the eggs, which have a deep red colour. A batch consists of about 100 eggs which hatch after approximately four days. The larvae are brought to a previously dug pit in which they remain for another three to four days. When free swimming the fry start feeding from the sediment on the bottom, efficiently guarded by their parents. At this stage they are already big enough to feed on newly hatched *Artemia*.

The small tributary in which we found *"Ae." biseriatus* is about 7 km from Istmina in the direction of Río Condoto. The water characteristics were as follows: pH 7.0, total hardness 1°, carbonate hardness 2°, no measurable nitrite, temperature 28.5° C, and air temperature 39° C (15.00 hr).

"Aequidens" biseriatus from the Río Condoto. Photo F. Ingemann Hansen.

Apistogramma iniridae Kullander, 1979

Tonny Brandt Andersen

Apistogramma iniridae is infrequently seen in aquaria, especially in Denmark where it has been impossible to obtain this species for many years. In the spring of 1991, however, three Danish aquarists collected it in its natural habitat: the Río Inirida drainage in Colombia. The fishes in the photograph below were collected in Caño Aqujón. The water in this stream has the following qualities: pH 5.3, total hardness: not measurable, carbonate hardness 4°, conductivity 10 µS, no measurable nitrite, and a temperature of 30° C.

A. iniridae is a cave spawner, which means that its aquarium must contain a small number of caves, so that the female can choose the best one for spawning. Like most other *Apistogramma*, *A. iniridae* is polygynous which means that a single male spawns with several females. It is recommended that each female be given a bottom area of 20 to 30 cm in diameter in the breeding tank.

Before spawning commences the female takes possession of a cave and makes this ready for the brood. The eggs are stuck to the ceiling of the cave with a thin thread. After about three days the eggs hatch. The female takes care of the fry, the male is not welcome to join in the brood care. The water quality of the breeding tank must closely match that of the natural environment. In this respect the pH and the temperature are the most important.

Breeders in Denmark have obtained variable results with *A. iniridae*: the spawns ranged from 15 to 197 fry, and the species has become re-established among aquarists.

The most distinctive marking of *A. iniridae* consists of a black longitudinal line which runs from the rear edge of the eye right onto the caudal peduncle. In this respect it differs from *A. pertensis* and *A. meinkeni*, which seem to be its closest relatives. *A. pertensis* and *A. meinkeni* have a black spot on the caudal peduncle and the longitudinal stripe stops clearly before the spot. Another characteristic of *A. iniridae* is the black bars on the lower half of the body which are visible only when the fish is excited. When these bars are prominent the horizontal line almost disappears.

A wild caught pair of *Apistogramma iniridae* from Caño Aqujón, Colombia (small photo). Photos F. Ingemann Hansen.

Livebearing cichlids?

Martin Geerts

Cichlids derive their popularity mainly from the care they bestow on their offspring. The brood care technique is not similar in all cichlids. There are substrate brooders, cave brooders, pit brooders, and mouthbrooders. The most advanced form of brood care, livebearing, is not found in any cichlid species. According to a recent publication by Professor E.K. Balon (1991) there are ample indications that the evolution of livebearing cichlids is just a matter of time: "Speculatively, given time, the evolution of livebearing cichlids can be expected". It appears that this author sees the cichlids on an evolutionary trajectory which starts at substrate brooding and ends at livebearing.

It is reasonable to assume that further improvements in brood care can only increase the success of cichlids. However, Jensen (1990) disagrees with this point of view. According to Jensen the cichlids belong to the suborder Labroidei. The labroid families in general are very rich in species. Jensen ascribes this richness to the pharyngeal specialisations which occur among these fishes. The surf perches, Embiotocidae, however, are an exception. Although these labroids also display all the pharyngeal specialisations which are so characteristic of the suborder Labroidei, they have failed to develop a species-rich family. In fact the surf perches are a species-poor fish family. Interestingly it is also the only labroid family which is livebearing. But livebearing is not the only feature in which the surf perches differ from other labroid families; it is thus not correct to ascribe their meagre speciation to the fact that they are livebearing (Jensen, 1990). Jensen's publication, however, makes it clear that labroid fishes can develop livebearing species, which puts Balon's ideas regarding the evolution of the cichlid's brood care in another perspective. Jensen further indicates that the success of cichlids would not necessarily be increased when they reached the livebearing stage.

Balon (1991) voiced his remarkable idea in a book which is entirely devoted to the coelacanth (*Latimeria chalumnae*). The coelacanth, probably the most talked about living fossil, is a fish with a truly remarkable breeding technique. Females of this species produce very large eggs which develop inside the reproductive system of the mother. Not all embryos develop at the same speed. Those that free themselves from the egg-shell first feed on their large yolk-sac before they fall upon the embryos which are still in a earlier phase of development (oophagy or adelphophagy). As a result of this breeding technique the coelacanth produces few offspring, but the young are born well developed and thus have an increased chance of becoming mature.

In order to explain the origin of this breeding biology Balon refers to some cichlids from Lake Tanganyika. He discusses four Tanganyika cichlids which he assumes to have a common ancestor. It seems that Balon regards the species flock of Lake Tanganyika as a monophyletic group which is most probably incorrect. Virtually all scientists share the opinion that the Tanganyika flock has a polyphyletic (developed from several ancestors) origin, and this was recently confirmed by Nishida (1991). The common ancestor referred to by Balon must therefore have lived before the formation of the lake.

The cichlids which participate in Balon's investigation are: *Boulengerochromis microlepis, Haplotaxodon microlepis, Tanganicodus irsacae* and *Cyphotilapia frontosa*. Balon gives the breeding biology for these species as, respectively, a sand-nest brooder, a pit brooder which "... guards its clutch in a sand-pit nest but after hatching collects the embryos into its buccal pouch and broods them" (i.e. larvophilous mouthbrooder; see remarks later), further a biparental mouthbrooder, and a maternal mouthbrooder.

B. microlepis produces an enormous quantity of small eggs. The hatched fry start their oral feeding when they have attained a length of 8.4 mm. By contrast *C. frontosa*, like the coelacanth, produces relatively large eggs but in small quantities. The eggs are brooded inside the female's mouth for more than 50 days (according to Balon). When the fry are released they have a length of 23.0 mm. Balon regards the breeding biology of *H. microlepis* and *T. irsacae* as intermediate stages between the sand nest brooding of *B. microlepis* and the maternal mouthbrooding of *C. frontosa*. Balon refers to Kuwamura (1988) when he describes the breeding biology of *Haplotaxodon microlepis* as being a larvophilous mouthbrooding. However, neither Kuwamura nor other authors have found *H. microlepis* or any other Tanganyika cichlid to be a larvophilous mouthbrooder.

Balon concludes from the breeding techniques of these four species that an intensification of the brood care leads to an increasing part of the early development taking place during the embryonal stage. Contrary to common practice he regards the end of the embryonic stage as beingwhen the young start collecting their own food and not when they hatch from the egg. Young fishes which have freed themselves from the egg-shell but haven't started feeding orally are called "eleuthero-embryos" (free-swimming embryos). If we adopt this view then it appears that the larval stage in maternal mouthbrooding species is totally abolished in favour of an increased chance of growing into mature fishes. During the larval period the brood is very vulnerable. Moreover the transition from larva to juvenile demands a lot of energy. Such a reproductive biology

also pages 51-52 of this volume), *Rhamphochromis* sp. (Spreinat, 1991), and *Cyprichromis* sp. (Konings, 1991). The fertilisation of the eggs of midwater spawners should take place immediately after they have been released and not in the female's mouth after they have been retrieved. According to this scenario the fertilisation would take place in close proximity to the female's genital pore. As Balon has pointed out the female invests more and more in the quality of the eggs. A logical consequence is that the number of eggs decreases. In the end each and every egg is of importance for the survival of the species. This could then be a reason for females to tend to retain the eggs in their reproductive tract while males exude their milt in the immediate vicinity of the female's genital pore. Eventually this could lead to live-bearing cichlids.

References

BALON E.K. (1991) Probable evolution of the coelacanth's reproductive style; lecithotrophy and orally feeding embryos in cichlid fishes and in *Latimeria chalumnae*. *Env. Biol. Biol. Fish* 32: 249-265.

ECCLES, D.H. & LEWIS, D.S.C. (1981) Midwater spawing in *Haplochromis chrysonotus* (Boulenger) (Teleostei: Cichlidae) in Lake Malawi. *Env. Biol. Fish.* Vol. 6, No. 2, pp 201-202.

JENSEN J. (1990) Plausibility and testability; Assessing the consequences of evolutionary innovations. pp. 171- 190 in M. Nitecki (ed), *Evolutionary Innovations.*

KONINGS, A. (1991) *Cyprichromis* sp. "Leptosoma Jumbo". pp 26-27 in: A. Konings (Ed.), The Cichlids Yearbook. Vol. 1. Cichlid Press, St. Leon-Rot, Germany.

KUWAMURA, T. (1988) Biparental mouthbrooding and guarding in a Tanganyikan cichlid *Haplotaxodon microlepis. Jap. J. Ichthyology*, Vol. 35, No. 1, pp 62-68.

KUWAMURA T. & MIHIGO N. (1988) Early ontogeny of a substrate-brooding cichlid, *Boulengerochromis microlepis*, compared with mouthbrooding species in Lake Tanganyika. *Physiol. Ecol. Japan.* 25: pp 19-25.

SPREINAT, A. (1991) Freilaichende *Rhamphochromis. DATZ* 44, pp 198-200.

Boulengerochromis microlepis, the largest known cichlid, might also be the most primitive in Lake Tanganyika. Photo Martin Geerts.

(mouthbrooding) requires eggs with a high quality type of yolk. In general such eggs are also larger, but Balon (pers. comm.) finds it inappropriate to give too much attention to egg-size (see also table 1 in Kuwamura & Mihigo, 1988). The comparison of Tanganyika cichlids with the coelacanth does not seem to explain the latter's breeding biology. After all the coelacanth is a livebearer.

So how could a livebearing cichlid evolve? A necessary step is probably pelagic spawning, i.e. the eggs are released in midwater. The females collect the eggs before they have reached the substrate. This has been described for *Copadichromis chrysonotus* (see: Eccles & Lewis, 1981; see

Cichlid Literatim

Reviews by Lee Finley

KULLANDER, S.O. and A.M.C. SILFVERGRIP. (1991) Review of the South American cichlid genus *Mesonauta* Günther (Teleostei, Cichlidae) with descriptions of two new species. *Rev. Suisse Zool.* 98 (2): pp 407-448.

Since its first introduction into the hobby in 1908 (with subsequent successful breeding in 1911) the *"festivum"* has remained a popular fish among both general aquarists and cichlid specialists. Those who currently enjoy this "species" will, courtesy of this revision, have a lot more to enjoy. Before looking at the body of this paper, a brief note is needed on the history of the genus *Mesonauta*. The genus was erected by Günther in 1862 to encompass *Heros insignis*, *H. festivus* (both described by Heckel in 1840), and *Chromys acora* (described by Castelnau in 1855). He placed all three species under the name *M. insignis*. Subsequent to this, the "fish" was usually placed by most ichthyologists in the genus *Cichlasoma* and the species name *festivum* was consistently used. In 1983 Kullander resurrected *Mesonauta* and in 1986 he validated both *insignis* and *festivus* as species. In 1986 Kullander also used, without discussion, the name *acora* in conjunction with *Mesonauta* and this was repeated by him and Nijssen in 1989. This brings us to the current paper wherein the authors validate these three species within *Mesonauta*, describe two more species and note that there are probably two or three more species that they are aware of!

In the paper under discussion, the authors provide a comprehensive diagnosis of the genus *Mesonauta* and state their feeling that it, along with *Pterophyllum*, *Symphysodon*, *Uaru*, and *Heros* (consisting of *H. severus* and *H. appendiculatus* only) probably forms a monophyletic assemblage among the cichlasomines. The generic diagnosis, in keeping with the past work of the senior author, is extremely thorough and provides good background material, much of which may be of use to aquarists. Of particular general interest (and of specific interest regarding the *Mesonauta* species) is the discussion of the vertical bar patterning amongst South American cichlids. A basic pattern of eight bars is discussed and the variation seen within these bars in *Mesonauta* is considered to be a valuable diagnostic tool in separating the species. In fact, the key to the genus, along with some "standard" characters (gill arch morphology, anal spine numbers, etc.), relies heavily on the barring pattern in species differentiation.

The species included in the genus (along with their known distribution) include: *M. insignis* (upper Rio Negro and Río Orinoco); *M. festivus* (Bolivian Amazonia including part of Peru, Guaporé-Mamoré and Paraguay drainages, Rio Jamar, and lower Rio Tapajós); *M. acora* (upper Rio Xingu and lower Rio Tocantins and probably Rio Araguaia. Note —The map in the paper (Fig. 10) appears to be somewhat at odds with the verbal locations); *M. egregius* (restricted area of Colombian llanos, tributaries of Río Meta and one tributary of the Río Vichada); and *M. mirificus* (sections of Peru and adjacent Colombia-middle Ucayali to near Leticia). In addition to these species the authors note the existence of at least three other undescribed species: one found in the Río Napo (Peru), which is sympatric with *M. mirificus*, and two others —one from the Xingu and another from the Tocantins. The latter is sympatric with *M. acora*. Due to a lack of adequate material no attempt was made to describe any of these additional "species".

It is beyond the scope of this short piece to go into the differentiation of the various species but anyone interested would be well advised to locate this particular paper. The pattern descriptions, coupled with line drawings and excellent black and white photos, should enable the aquarist to do a pretty good job of species determination, even if locality data are poor or missing. Of course, there are the (at least?) three undefined species and populational variation among those known, but it does provide an excellent start.

STIASSNY, M.L.J. and C.L. GERSTNER. (1992) The parental care behaviour of *Paratilapia polleni* (Perciformes, Labroidei), a phylogenetically primitive cichlid from Madagascar, with a discussion of the evolution of maternal care in the family Cichlidae. *Env. Biol. Fish.* 34: pp 219-233.

The cichlids of Madagascar are one of the last great frontiers that await cichlid aquarists. Their past availability in the hobby has been beyond scant to non-existent. But due to some livestock brought to the U.S. for research by the American Museum of Natural History (New York, N.Y.) this situation has, at least in a small way, been improved. Some fry, which resulted as a part of the study on which this review is based, have started to make their way to hobbyists and hopefully these will become established and increase availability in the near future.

Paratilapia polleni, from a phylogenetic point of view, is generally considered to be a primitive cichlid. This placement is based on a number of anatomical features, none of which would be readily apparent to aquarists. (See Stiassny, M.L.J. (1991) Phylogenetic interrelationships of the family Cichlidae: an overview. pp 1-35. In: M.H.A. Keenleyside (Ed.) *Cichlid Fishes: Behaviour, Ecology and Evolution*. Chapman & Hall). In any case it is given a basal position in what appears to be the generally accepted cladogram of cichlid relationships. (A cladogram is basically a kind of family tree.) The authors were very interested in *P. polleni*'s reproduction in that it was thought that it might shed some light on the plesiomorphic (or primitive) state of parental care in cichlids. In the majority of bony fishes where parental care is provided it is the male that handles the primary care. Cichlids are "unusual" in that the female plays a major (and often exclusive) role in this area. Would males of *P. polleni* display a major role in the care of eggs and fry in that it is "primitive"? This was the apparent idea at the root of this study, that is, the assumption that strong male care may be more involved with "primitive" cichlids. The results proved interesting. In *P. polleni* the female participation in brood care is strong and well developed and can only be classed as primary in nature. Some minor differences in male and female roles, compared to similar studies on other cichlids, were noted but none of these was major enough to even hint at a greater male involvement. Caution is, of course, needed when describing captive behavioural studies on a small number of specimens as they might relate to natural reproduction in the wild, but overall the authors seem satisfied with their results. Based on this the authors cautiously suggest that the female dominance in the brood care of cichlids evolved in the distant past and pre-dates the origin of known living cichlids. Of course, there are at least eight additional species of cichlids known from Madagascar which await study and who knows what surprises may await us. There is one group (Ptychochromines—two genera, one species each) which the authors place even more basally than the group to which *Paratilapia* belongs, and even though the authors expect no surprises ..... who knows until the work is done?

There are a few interesting points to be taken from the article. First are the methods used. The descriptions of the parental guarding cycle are concise and might well serve as a model for aquarists wanting to document the spawning and care cycles for other substratum spawning cichlids. The paper is worth having in your library for the methods and descriptions of various behaviours given. Secondly, the eggs of *P. polleni* are quite interesting. The female extrudes a "continuous egg string" in which the eggs (about 1000 in the reported spawning) are attached to an "adhesive central fiber bundle" by "thinner fiber bundles". This is not attached to the substrate and through fanning by the female it becomes "intertwined with itself" and the eggs become "pulled together into a dense mass three or four layers deep". This mass does not adhere in any way and is easily moved by the vigorous pectoral fanning of the female. Thereby an interesting "mobile egg mass" is created. Results of similar, or differing, reproductive processes in other Madagascan cichlids will be eagerly awaited.

Paratilapia polleni. This species was introduced in the aquaristic hobby by J.-C. Nourisat.

CICHLID ORGANIZATIONS WORLDWIDE

Australia
The New South Wales Cichlid Society
P.O. Box 163
Moorebank, N.S.W. 2170

Queensland Cichlid Group
P.O. Box 163
Wooloongabba, Queensland 4102

Victorian Cichlid Society
23 Mangana Drive
Mulgrave, Victoria 3170

Austria
Deutsche Cichliden Gesellschaft
Victor Kaplan Straße 1-9/1/3/12
A-1220 Wien

Belgium
Belgische Cichliden Vereninging
Kievitlaan 23
B-2228 Ranst

Czechoslovakia
SZCH Klub Chovatelov Cichlíd
Príkopova 2
CS-831 03 Bratislava

Denmark
Dansk Cichlide Selskab
Töllösevej 76.
DK-2700 Brönshöj

France
Association France Cichlid
15 Rue des Hirondelles
F-67350 Dauendorf

Germany
Deutsche Cichliden Gesellschaft
Eberescheweg 41
D(W)-4200 Oberhausen

Hungary
Hungarian Cichlid Association
Lukács László, Karolina út 65
H-1113 Budapest

Netherlands
Nederlandse Cichliden Vereniging
Boeier 31
NL-1625 CJ Hoorn

Sweden
Nordiska CiklidSällskapet
Skogsgläntan 16
S-435 38 Mölnlycke

Switzerland
Deutsche Cichliden Gesellschaft
Am Balsberg 1
CH-8302 Kloten

Taiwan (R.O.C.)
Taiwanese Cichlid Association
N°17, Lane 239, An-Ho Road
Taipei

United Kingdom
British Cichlid Association
100 Keighley Road
Skipton, North Yorkshire, BD23 2RA

U. S. A.
American Cichlid Association
P.O. Box 32130
Raleigh, NC 27622

Adv. Cichl. Aquarists South California
P.O. Box 8173
San Marino, CA 91108

Apistogramma Study Group
1845 Jaynes Road
Mosinee, WI 54455

Cichlasoma Study Group
6432 South Holland Court
Littlerton, CO 80123

Fort Wayne Cichlid Association
9638 Manor Woods Rdf.
Ft. Wayne, IN 46804

Greater Chicago Cichlid Association
2633 N. Rhodes
River Grove, IL 60171

Greater Cincinnati Cichlid Association
15 W. Southern Avenue
Covington, KY 41015

Illinois Cichlids and Scavengers
7807 Sunset Drive
Elmwood Park, IL 60635

Michigan Cichlid Association
P.O. Box 59
New Baltimore, MI 48047

Ohio Cichlid Association
3896 Boston Rd.
Brunswick, OH 44212

Pacific Coast Cichlid Association
P.O. Box 28145
San Jose, CA 95128

Rocky Mountain Cichlid Association
5065 W. Hinsdale Cir.
Littleton, CO 80123

Southern California Cichlid Association
P.O. Box 574
Midway City, CA 92655

Texas Cichlid Association
6845 Winchester
Dallas, TX 75231